Self-harm and Suicide

ISSUES
(formerly Issues for the Nineties)

Volume 51

Editor

Craig Donnellan

Independence
Educational Publishers

First published by Independence
PO Box 295
Cambridge CB1 3XP
England

British Library Cataloguing in Publication Data
Self-harm and Suicide – (Issues Series)
I. Donnellan, Craig II. Series
362.2'8

ISBN 1 86168 132 1

Printed in Great Britain
The Burlington Press
Cambridge

Typeset by
Claire Boyd

Cover
The illustration on the front cover is by
Pumpkin House.

CONTENTS

Chapter One: Self-harm and Suicide

Chapter Two: Seeking Help

Introduction

Self-harm and Suicide is the fifty-first volume in the **Issues** series. The aim of this series is to offer up-to-date information about important issues in our world.

Self-harm and Suicide looks at the issues of self-harm and suicide and seeking help.

The information comes from a wide variety of sources and includes:
Government reports and statistics
Newspaper reports and features
Magazine articles and surveys
Literature from lobby groups
and charitable organisations.

It is hoped that, as you read about the many aspects of the issues explored in this book, you will critically evaluate the information presented. It is important that you decide whether you are being presented with facts or opinions. Does the writer give a biased or an unbiased report? If an opinion is being expressed, do you agree with the writer?

Self-harm and Suicide offers a useful starting-point for those who need convenient access to information about the many issues involved. However, it is only a starting-point. At the back of the book is a list of organisations which you may want to contact for further information.

*****

Suicide and attempted suicide

Information from the Royal College of Psychiatrists

How often does it happen?

In Western Europe, over the last 40 years, there has been a huge increase in the number of young people who try to kill themselves. Rates vary enormously from country to country. In the UK, it causes about 150,000 hospital attendances every year. Poisoning with paracetamol is the commonest type of overdose in Britain. Paracetamol causes serious liver damage and each year this leads to many deaths. Even a small number of tablets can be fatal.

The number of young people who actually die after attempting suicide is very small in the UK. Suicide is extremely rare in children under the age of 14. This is probably because young children tend to show distress in other ways – by crying or protesting, for example. They lack the ability to plan or carry out complex tasks on their own and don't understand the permanence of death. When young children kill themselves, it is usually by accident, sometimes because a game has gone tragically wrong.

There are many more suicides in teenagers. Among 15-19-year-olds, there are more than 13 suicides per 100,000 youngsters each year. Young men in this age group are even more at risk. They are less likely to show their distress beforehand than girls.

The risk of suicide is higher when a young person:

- is depressed, or when they have a serious mental illness – if they get the help and treatment they need, the risk can be greatly reduced;
- is using drugs or alcohol when they are upset;
- has tried to kill themselves a number of times or has planned for a while about how to die without being saved;
- has a relative or friend who tried to kill themselves.

Why do people try to kill themselves?

Nearly everyone has times when they feel sad and lonely. Sometimes it can feel as if no one really likes us, that we are a failure, that we just upset people and that no one would care if we were dead. We may feel angry but unable to say so, or feel hopeless about the future.

It is feelings like these that make some young people try to kill themselves. Often, several upsetting things have happened over a short time and one more upset or rejection is the 'last straw'. An argument with parents is a common example. Another is breaking up with a friend, or being in trouble. Teenagers who try to kill themselves are often trying to cope independently with very upset feelings or difficult problems for the first time. They don't know how to solve their problems or lack the support they need to cope with a big upset. They feel overwhelmed and see no other way out.

Often, the decision to attempt suicide is made quickly without thinking. At the time, many people just want their problems to disappear, and have no idea how to get help. They feel as if the only way out is to kill themselves.

Is this just attention-seeking?

Nowadays, it is common for hospitals to see young people who have tried to kill themselves because they have been feeling desperate and unhappy. In most cases the young person soon regrets it. Sometimes, they don't really want to die, but want to do something to show their distress and 'make people care'. Any attempt should always be taken very seriously. The young person needs an adult to understand what they have been feeling, although

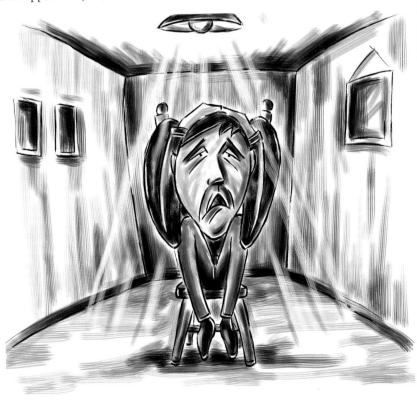

they might find it hard to put into words. They need someone to give constructive help.

Who is most at risk?

There are three main groups:

- In about 1 in 5 cases, the young person will have shown no previous sign of emotional or behavioural difficulties. They are upset by common problems with friends or parents, under stress from exams, or have suffered rejection or bereavement. If the young person is able to talk about their problems and get help, they are unlikely to repeat the attempt.
- In about 3 in 5 cases, the young person has been showing signs of emotional or behavioural problems for months before the attempt, and has not been able to find help. These young people usually need specialist help such as counselling or psychiatric treatment for depression or other mental health problems.
- In about 1 in 5 cases, the person has had serious problems (e.g. with the police, their family or school) for a long time. These are the young people who are most at risk of further attempts. Some will already be seeing a counsellor, psychiatrist or social worker. Others have refused normal forms of help and appear to be trying to run away from their problems. Some seek an escape through drugs or alcohol. Young people who are misusing drugs or alcohol have the highest risk of death by suicide.

Specialist help available

Everyone who has tried to kill themselves or taken an overdose needs an urgent assessment by a doctor as soon as possible even if they look OK. The harmful effects can sometimes be delayed. Even small amounts of some medication can be fatal.

All young people who attempt suicide or harm themselves should have a specialist mental health assessment before leaving the hospital. Often, a psychiatrist from the local child and adolescent mental health service will do this. The aim is to discover the causes of the problems and to prevent repetition. It is very helpful when parents or carers can take part. This makes it easier to understand the background to what has happened, and to work out together whether help is needed after the young person leaves hospital. Usually, help will be offered by the person from the child and adolescent mental health service who has carried out the assessment.

Treatment can make all the difference. A lot of young people make another attempt if they do not receive the help they need. Usually, treatment will involve individual or family work for a small number of sessions. A very small number of young people who try to kill themselves really do still want to die. Often, they are suffering from depression or another treatable mental health problem. They may need specialist help over a longer period of time.

- The above information is an extract from the Royal College of Psychiatrists web site which can be found at www.rcpsych.ac.uk

Half of all women 'think of suicide'

By Tara Womersley

The majority of women have suffered from some degree of depression and nearly half have contemplated suicide, according to a survey. Most women did not know why they felt so low, although others cited work, money worries and relationships as the likely reasons. Of 1,000 questioned, 41 per cent had taken anti-depressants and 17 per cent had telephoned the Samaritans for help.

Relationships were often fraught, with those who had husbands or boyfriends arguing two to three times a month and 13 per cent of women claiming that they wanted to split up. Many were unhappy at work. More than a quarter of women said that they wanted to leave their jobs and almost half had phoned in sick because they could not bear the thought of going to work.

Half of the women in the survey for *She* magazine said they comfort-ate when they felt depressed, while 42 per cent said they went shopping. Two-thirds had suffered from sleepless nights; more than a third blamed money worries for their insomnia and 28 per cent blamed their partners.

David Boggis, who edits a newsletter for the Fellowship of Depressives Anonymous, said he was not surprised by the findings. Women tended to be more open about depression, which could be one of the reasons why the British suicide rate was higher for males than females, he added.

'About two-thirds of our members are women. They tend to contact us much more than men so that they can be put in touch with others who are in a similar position. It is true that the suicide rate for men is higher but that may well be because women open up more. Insomnia can be just one of the symptoms of depression. The problem with comfort-eating is that a woman eats when she has a low self-esteem but will then look in the mirror and feel worse.'

Alison Pylkkanen, editor of *She* magazine, said that just because so many women had thought about suicide at some point it did not mean they were going to kill themselves. 'What we found was that women were brutally honest,' she added. 'Unfortunately many of them said that they were too aware of how precious people's time was, which was why they did not want to go to their doctor and discuss their problems because they felt guilty about the long waiting lists.'

Defining suicide

Information from The Samaritans

Introduction

Suicide n. 1. the act or an instance of killing oneself intentionally.
(*Collins English Dictionary*)

A dictionary definition of suicide appears so simple. Yet, to take one's own life is not simple. It is a tragic event which affects literally millions of people – nearly one in three people in this country know someone who has taken their own life. The ripples of every suicide are wide; and those who are left behind often have to deal with their own emotions for the rest of their lives.

In 1997 6,426 people in the UK and the Republic of Ireland took their own lives. Or rather, 6,426 deaths were defined as suicide. In practice, this means that there were 6,426 recorded cases of death by suicide and self-inflicted injury or injury by other and unspecified means, undetermined whether accidentally or purposely inflicted.

Confused? It's not surprising. Perhaps defining suicide is not as simple as it first seemed.

So where do these figures come from? Well, the Office for National Statistics compiles its figures from information it gathers from coroners' offices. But how much information do coroners have to make their decision on? Perhaps concerns for the bereaved families may make some coroners less willing to record suicide verdicts? And how consistent are the records? Scotland and Northern Ireland have their own differing systems and ways of assessing suicides – does this mean we are getting different readings for different areas of the UK?

The problems of accurate figures go further. Recently published research has shown an increase in suicide among young men, whilst other research has highlighted a major problem of suicide among rural workers and young Asian women. Problems like alcoholism and homelessness are known to be contributory factors to many cases of suicide. But how much faith can we have in this research, and what is happening with it? Is it changing the way organisations work? Is it affecting the direction of government policy?

These questions appear before even considering the statistics for those people who have attempted to take their own life. Over 140,000 people were admitted to casualty departments in the UK in 1997 as a result of harming themselves. But how many more people are never seen by a doctor, or visit a hospital?

60,000 people have killed themselves in the last 10 years in the UK and Republic of Ireland

---

Ask someone which organisations they think exist to help people with suicidal feelings and they will mention The Samaritans. But people who are potentially suicidal could come into contact with many public, health and voluntary organisations. Up to 60% of people who take their own lives have consulted their GP in the 3 months prior to their death. What training does that GP have in dealing with that patient?

The same questions could be asked about all health workers, or about professions like prison officers, who are dealing with people at high risk of suicide every day. And then there is the question of education. What does the general public know about the risks of suicide? What part do the media play in all this? Reports on suicides are a small but staple part of the average newspaper diet. What responsibilities do journalists have in reporting this difficult area? Do they know enough about it? Do they know, for instance, that suicide kills 70 per cent more people than road accidents? Should they be reporting more on the risks of suicide to help educate people or should they be reporting suicide less to avoid copycat attempts?

And more generally, what can people and organisations do to eradicate the stigma that is still attached to suicide?

60,000 people have killed themselves in the last 10 years in the UK and Republic of Ireland.

Suicidal behaviour in children and young people

The following article was written by the charity Kidscape and is reproduced here by kind permission

Suicide is the third leading cause of death in the young in the United Kingdom (traffic accidents and cancer being the first and second). Yet, adults are often surprised and horrified that children can and do kill themselves.

Why?

We can never know all the causes, but it may be that the child or young person is:

- depressed because of social problems with friends
- worried about school pressures and examinations
- concerned about family problems such as divorce
- being bullied
- a victim of child abuse
- overwhelmed by the world situation
- experiencing a chemical imbalance
- having a drug or alcohol-related problem
- influenced by another suicide story
- trying to make life easier for someone
- trying to escape from an impossible situation
- trying to get help for some problem
- trying to manipulate someone for hurting them
- acting on sudden, inexplicable impulse
- putting pressure on themselves.

Possible indicators

The following are common characteristics of many people who commit suicide:

- experienced the loss of a loved one through divorce or death
- overly sensitive to emotional pain or upheavals
- unable to find friendship or security
- unable to deal with problems and feel hopeless
- convinced that suicide is the only solution
- given indications or said that they wished to die.

What to look for

Although some children may not give any indication that they are considering suicide, be aware of the following signs:

- change in eating or sleeping patterns
- loss of interest in activities usually enjoyed
- irritability, sadness, hopelessness
- loss of energy; feeling tired and listless
- unable to concentrate or sudden poor school performance
- restless, pacing type of behaviour
- excessive self-blame for everything
- continued thoughts of suicide or death
- giving away precious possessions.

Most of these signs could be due to other causes, but if a child or young person is exhibiting three or four of these consistently over a period of a week to ten days, there is cause for concern. Often young people who try to kill themselves don't really want to die and do not understand the finality of death.

What to do

If a child talks about suicide, take it very seriously. There is a myth that 'talking about suicide means the person won't do it'. People who talk about suicide do kill themselves. Immediately seek help through your local Child Guidance Clinic or one of the Help Organisations listed at the end of this article.

- encourage talking by saying: 'I'd like to hear about it'
- give the child a chance to be alone with you
- be direct: 'I'm worried about you'
- set limits – they help children feel secure
- help the child find solutions/offer alternatives
- don't force a child into an impossible situation. It may result in them feeling that suicide is the only escape. For example, severe bullying might make going to school a nightmare. If you cannot get the school to address the problem, either change schools or educate your child at home
- trust your own judgements
- remove means of suicide, if possible
- tell others and seek professional help. Don't try and cope alone
- encourage children to eat and sleep properly
- encourage physical or recreational activity to release tension
- role-play with them how to cope with situations
- encourage crying, deep breathing exercises, laughter, listening to music, drawing, relaxation techniques, teach positive assertion skills
- teach problem-solving skills by explaining how to find alternatives and to foresee consequences
- build up a child's self-confidence. Find something the child is good at and praise him/her.

Help organisations

The Samaritans offer a twenty-four-hour help line for anyone with suicidal problems, or for anyone who wants to talk. Some branches have drop-in centres. See your local telephone directory or telephone 0345 909090.

Youth Access (Young people's counselling) can refer you to an agency in your area. Telephone 020 8772 9900.

MIND run an information service for anyone concerned with mental health issues. Telephone Head Office on 020 8519 2122

ext. 275, or 020 8522 1728 if you live in Greater London, or 0345 660163 if you live outside Greater London.

Child Line is a twenty-four-hour help line for children and young people in distress. Call 0800 1111.

The British Association of Counselling can be contacted for a list of help organisations and counsellors in your area. Send a large SAE to 1 Regent Place, Rugby, Warwickshire. CV21 2PJ or telephone 01788 578328/9.

Key facts: attempted suicide

Information from The Samaritans

Definition

- Attempted suicide, parasuicide and deliberate self-harm are all terms which are often used interchangeably. They all describe non-fatal acts of self-harm which arise for a variety of different reasons. 'Suicidal' people also have varying degrees of the wish to die, and these acts can involve different degrees of risk to life.
- The WHO definition of parasuicide[1] is as follows: 'An act with non-fatal outcome, in which an individual deliberately initiates a non-habitual behaviour that, without intervention from others, will cause self-harm ... and which is aimed at realising changes which the subject desired via the actual or expected physical consequences.'

Suicide risk

- Several studies[2] have shown that approximately one out of every 100 suicide attempters will die by suicide within a year of an attempt, a suicide risk approximately 100 times that of the general population.
- The highest risk occurs during the first three years following a suicide attempt, particularly in the first six months. Factors associated with higher suicide risk following an attempt are: being male, long-term use of hypnotics, poor physical health and repeat attempts.[3]

Prevalence of attempted suicide

- There are no national statistics of attempted suicide, however

national figures can be estimated from locally-collected figures. In general, these data refer to instances where a person has been taken to the accident and emergency department of a general hospital as a result of a suicide attempt. They do not include attempts which happened in psychiatric hospitals or those which were treated by GPs in the community. This means that true figures are probably higher.

- Recent estimates of national figures, based on locally-collected data, suggest that 142,000 people per year are seen in hospitals in England and Wales following an episode of self-harm (i.e. self-poisoning and self-injury).[4]
- Another study estimates that there are 170,000 cases of self-poisoning alone, which are referred to general hospitals in the UK.[5]

The following data are taken from the Oxford Monitoring System.[6] The pattern of attempted suicide in Oxford has been shown to be reasonably representative of what is happening elsewhere in the UK.[7]

- There has recently been an upturn in attempted suicide, with the rate by males increasing by 62% and the rate by females increasing by 42% between 1985 and 1995. The largest increase has been in the rate of attempts by young men and boys aged 15-24, where the rate has nearly tripled, by 194%.[4]

Age and sex variations

- The majority of suicide attempters are young, with 68%

being under 35 years of age.[6]
- Since the 1970s, women and girls have always shown higher rates of attempted suicide, with a ratio of more than 2:1, however currentlÉXthe ratio of female to male cases is relatively low, at 1.36:1.[6]
- All of the increase in male attempted suicide has been in younger males, with a particularly marked rise in 15-24-year-olds which started in the mid 1980s. Since then the rate of attempted suicide for these young men has nearly tripled, rising by 194%.[4]
- Amongst women, rates have risen for 15-24-year-olds and 35-54-year-olds since the beginning of the 1990s, though these rises are less marked than those for men.[6]
- The group at highest risk of attempted suicide is young women aged between 15 and 19.[6]
- Males tend to report higher levels of suicide intent than females although the level of intent amongst the group of attempters tends to be moderate to low and does not differ greatly from that measured in the 1970s.[6]

Children

- The past three years have shown an increasing number of children and very young adolescents making suicide attempts. 1995 showed the highest recorded figure in Oxford of 71 children under 16 years of age. There was a slight decrease in 1996 to 64.[6]
- While the majority in this group are girls, there has been a marked increase in attempted suicide by boys.[6]

- 69% of overdoses by children involved paracetamol.[6]
- The youngest recorded attempter on the Oxford Monitoring System in 1996 was 11 years old.[6]

Methods

- Roughly 9 out of 10 attempts are by self-poisoning, 1 in 10 by self-injury and a small proportion (4%) by both types of method. Self-injury is more common in males than females.[6]
- The use of paracetamol for attempted suicide is growing, and was used for self-poisoning in half of all cases in 1996. Interestingly, however, the rate dropped slightly in 1996, when there was considerable publicity about the dangers of paracetamol poisoning.[6]

Repetition of attempts

- There has been an increase in the number of times people are making repeat attempts at suicide, indicating that intervention and treatment may be failing. The increase is also worrying in that the number of repeats is related to the likelihood of eventually dying by suicide.[4]
- There is also a rise in the number of first-time attempters, showing a growth in the population of people who have self-harmed and who are now at increased risk of suicide.[4]

Factors associated with suicide attempts

- The most frequent problem identified by the attempter is relationship difficulty (74% of cases), most usually with a partner (49%). In the past, this problem was reported most often by women but over the years men have been reporting such problems with increasing frequency, such that relationship difficulties with a partner are now reported by 50% of men.[6]
- Problems with other family members were reported more often by females.[6]
- Other problems are to do with employment or studies, alcohol, drugs and finances (more often reported by men), eating disorders (5% of women and girls) and

problems from the consequences of childhood sexual abuse (reported by 9% of women and 3.5% of the men).[6]
- The majority of suicide attempters are single, and rates of attempts were high for those who were divorced or separated. Married people have the lowest risk.[6]
- 43% of males who attempted suicide in 1996 were misusers of alcohol, as were 28% of females. Roughly a quarter of the males who attempted and a fifth of the females were known to be drinking more than the maximum safe limits. 11% of the men and 5% of the women were alcohol dependent at the time of the attempt.[6]
- Attempted suicide has been shown to be associated with social deprivation,[8] and unemployment.[7]

References
1. Kerkhof, AJFM, Schmidtke, A, Bille-Brahe, U, De Leo, D, Lonnqvist, J, (1994), 'Attempted Suicide in Europe: Findings from the Multicentre Study on Parasuicide by the WHO Regional Office for Europe', DSWO Press, Leiden.
2. Hawton, K, 'Suicide and attempted suicide', in *Handbook of Affective Disorders*, ed ES Paykel, Churchill Livingstone, 1992.
3. Hawton, K and Fagg, J, (1988), 'Suicide, and Other Causes of Death, Following Attempted Suicide', *British Journal of Psychiatry*, 152, 359-66.
4. Hawton, K, Fagg, J, Simkin, S, Bale, E, and Bond, A, (1997), 'Trends in deliberate self-harm in Oxford, 1985-1995', *British Journal of Psychiatry*, 171, 556-60.
5. Kapur, N, House, A, Creed, F, Feldman, E, Friedman, T, Guthrie, E, (1998), 'Management of deliberate self poisoning in adults in four teaching hospitals: descriptive study', *British Medical Journal*, 316: 831-2.
6. Hawton, K, Fagg, J, Simkin, S, Harriss, L, Bale, E and Bond, A, (unpublished) 'Deliberate Self-Harm in Oxford 1996', University Department of Psychiatry, Warneford Hospital, Oxford.
7. Platt, S, Hawton, K, Kreitman, N, Fagg, J, and Foster, J, (1988), 'Recent clinical and epidemiological trends in parasuicide in Edinburgh and Oxford: a tale of two cities', *Psychological Medicine*, 18, 405-18.
8. Gunnell, D J, Peters, T J, Kammerling, R M and Brooks, J, (1995), 'Relation between parasuicide, suicide, psychiatric admissions, and socioeconomic deprivation', *British Medical Journal*, 311, 226-30.

© The Samaritans

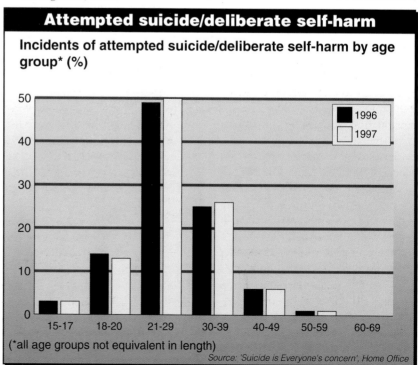

Attempted suicide/deliberate self-harm

Incidents of attempted suicide/deliberate self-harm by age group* (%)

(*all age groups not equivalent in length)

Source: 'Suicide is Everyone's concern', Home Office

Deliberate self-harm in young people

Deliberate self-harm is a term used when someone intentionally injures or harms themselves. Common examples include 'overdosing' (self-poisoning), hitting, cutting or burning oneself, pulling hair or picking skin, and self-strangulation. It can also include taking illegal drugs and excessive amounts of alcohol. Self-harm is always a sign of something being seriously wrong.

How often does it happen?

It's hard to say exactly, because most people keep their self-harm very private. Some say as many as 1 teenager in 10 could be affected. Health professionals probably see only the tip of the iceberg, and certainly nothing like this number. The problem mainly affects girls and is rare in boys (7:1 female:male ratio). It is very much more common than suicide.

Why do young people harm themselves?

It is not necessarily attention-seeking. Self-injury is a way of dealing with very difficult feelings that build up inside. People say different things about why they do it. Some say that they have been feeling desperate about a problem and don't know where to turn for help. They feel trapped and helpless. Self-injury helps them to feel more in control. Others talk of feelings of anger or tension that get bottled up inside until they feel like exploding. Self-injuring relieves this tension. Feelings of guilt or shame may also become unbearable. Self-harm is a way of punishing oneself. Some people try to cope with very upsetting experiences like trauma or abuse by convincing themselves that the upsetting event(s) never happened. These people sometimes suffer from feelings of numbness or deadness. They say that they feel detached from the world and their bodies, and that self-injury is a way of feeling more connected and alive.

Self-injury is always a sign of great upset. Sometimes people can end up killing themselves accidentally. The difficult feelings that lead to self-harm can be caused by a number of things. Young people who are depressed or have an eating disorder are at risk. So are people who take illegal drugs or excessive amounts of alcohol. In fact, eating disorders and drug or alcohol misuse are a kind of self-harm in themselves. The commonest trigger is an argument with a parent or close friend. When family life involves a lot of abuse, neglect or rejection, people are more likely to harm themselves. 'Copy cat' self-harm sometimes happens in a group. It can have tragic results.

Why they need help

Anyone who is harming themselves is struggling to cope and needs help. If people don't get help when they need it, problems are likely to continue. Problems may also get a lot worse and the effects may 'snowball'. Some people will continue to harm themselves more and more seriously. They may even end up killing themselves.

© 2000 Royal College of Psychiatrists

How many people self-harm?

Deliberate self-harm

Deliberate self-harm is used to describe all acts of self-harm, self-injury and attempted suicide. Statistics for self-harm are generally unreliable, as it often occurs in the home and does not reach the attention of services.

- Approximately 142,000 hospital admissions each year in England and Wales are the result of deliberate self-harm, mainly self-injury and drug overdoses.[1] Approximately 19,000 of these are young people.
- Self-harm is more common in women than in men;[2] it has been suggested that these differences are becoming less marked.
- 1 in 10 adolescents who have deliberately harmed themselves will do so on more than one occasion.[3]
- Adolescents who self-harm are more at risk of developing 'mental disorders' and 'personality disturbance' in later life, including behavioural problems and 'major affective disorders'.[3] There is often a background of abuse and family dysfunction.

Self-injury

Self-injury is a specific form of self-harm whereby people inflict wounds upon themselves by cutting, bruising or scratching themselves.

- A survey of women who self-injured found that 90% had cut themselves, a third had inflicted blows or scalded themselves; 74% had begun self-injuring during childhood or adolescence (0-19 years) and 69% had been inflicting injuries on themselves for more than five years.[4]

References
1 Hawton, K., Fagg, J., Simkin, S., Bale, E. & Bond. A. 'Trends in deliberate self-harm in Oxford, 1985-1995.' British Journal of Psychiatry (1997) 171:556-60.
2 The Samaritans, 'Information Resource Pack,' 1998.
3 Wood, A. 'Project Summary Randomised Controlled trial of group therapy for adolescents who repeatedly harm themselves.' Unpublished. 1997.
4 Arnold, I., 'Women and Self-Injury: a survey of 76 women.' Bristol Crisis Service for Women. 1995.

- The above is an extract from *The Fundamental Facts*, by Bird, L, produced by the Mental Health Foundation. ©*Mental Health Foundation, 2000*

Worried about self-injury?

Information from Young Minds

What is self-injury?

Self-injury is a way of dealing with very difficult feelings that build up inside. People deal with these feelings in various ways. Here are some examples:

- Cutting or burning themselves
- Bruising themselves
- Taking an overdose of tablets
- Pulling hair, or picking skin.

Some people think that the seriousness of the problem can be measured by how bad the injury is. This is not the case – a person who hurts themselves a bit can be feeling just as bad as someone who hurts themselves a lot.

Self-injury can affect anyone. It is a lot more common than people think. Many people hurt themselves secretly for a long time before finding the courage to tell someone.

Why do people do it?

'I think control's a big thing. You can't control what's happening around you, but you can control what you do to yourself.'

Everyone has problems in their lives and often people look for help. But sometimes it's hard to cope or even to put feelings into words. If they get bottled up inside, the pressure goes up and up until they feel like they might explode. This is the point where some people injure themselves.

'I didn't think there was any way out of my situation, so I took loads of tablets. I felt so bad I just wanted to die . . . and I nearly did. Now things are different, and I'm so glad to be alive.'

What makes people so stressed?

There are lots of things:

- Bullying
- Bereavement
- Housing problems
- Abuse
- Problems to do with race, culture or religion
- Growing up
- Money
- Pressure to fit in
- Sexual feelings
- Problems with friends
- Pressures at school or work

When a lot of problems come together, they can feel too much. If you're also feeling vulnerable, it's hard to cope as well as you normally do.

Thinking about stopping

There are lots of reasons why you might want to stop injuring yourself, although you might not know what else to do to help you cope. Here are some feelings that you might recognise . . .

- Hating yourself . . . for not being what people want
- Afraid . . . that you might end up dead

- Guilty . . . because you can't stop harming yourself, even if you want to
- Helpless . . . you don't know what to do for the best
- Embarrassed . . . in case people think you're weird
- Isolated . . . you don't know who to talk to
- Depressed . . . about anything ever getting better
- Out of control . . . you might not know why you hurt yourself and wonder if you're going mad
- Upset . . . you can't keep your feelings in . . . or maybe you can't let them out
- Scared . . . because you don't know why you do it . . . it's getting worse
- Worried . . . in case people think you're 'just attention-seeking'

'It helps a lot when I can be with someone I trust. I need people to understand me, support me. I need to be treated normally – just like anyone else. Not like a mad person. I'm not mad. I've just got problems because of what happened in my past. Something happens – and suddenly all the memories and feelings come back.'

When self-injury becomes a way of coping with stress it is a sign that there are problems that need sorting out. Help or support may be needed from family, friends, or others.

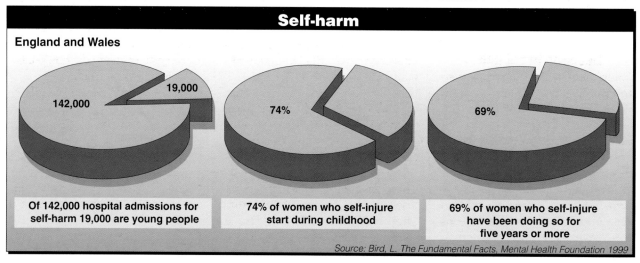

Self-harm

England and Wales

142,000 — 19,000

Of 142,000 hospital admissions for self-harm 19,000 are young people

74%

74% of women who self-injure start during childhood

69%

69% of women who self-injure have been doing so for five years or more

Source: Bird, L. The Fundamental Facts, Mental Health Foundation 1999

Helping yourself

If you have worries that make you want to injure yourself, you might want help to change. This section is about what you can do to help yourself.

Thinking about why you do it

Lots of people don't know why they harm themselves and it can be scary to become aware of how you feel and why. Stopping self-injury is easier if you can find other ways of coping. To do this, you'll first need to have a clear idea of why you do it. Many people find it useful to talk to someone who is trained to help.

Here are some questions that may be helpful for you to think about:

- What was happening when you first began to feel like injuring yourself?
- What seems to trigger the feeling of wanting to hurt yourself now?
- Are you always at a certain place or with a particular person?
- Do you have frightening memories or thoughts and feel you can't tell anyone?
- Is there anything else that makes you want to hurt yourself?

What helps you not hurt yourself?

When you feel upset, what helps you to cope? Some people find it helpful to be with a friend, talk to someone they trust, make a phone call, exercise, or do something else they enjoy. Others find it helps to paint or draw, listen to music or write feelings down in a diary or letter (even if it's not to send). What helps you?

Deciding to get help

Sometimes, however hard you try to stop injuring yourself on your own, you can't.

'The feeling of wanting to hurt myself would build up. I could put off doing it for a while but I couldn't last forever. I knew I had to get help.'

If you feel like this, it probably means that you need to talk to someone you can trust. This needs to be someone who will listen to you, talk about how you feel and give practical help. There could be a real risk that you could harm yourself permanently or perhaps even die.

If you feel your life is in danger it is very important to get help. You can make an emergency appointment to see your doctor.

Who can you trust to listen?

'Cutting myself is such a private thing. I find it hard to talk to other people about how I feel. They don't understand. They think I'm seeking attention – that's the last thing I want.'

When you have thought of someone to talk to, it helps to be prepared:

1. Where and when would you tell them?
2. Would you tell them face to face, by phone, or letter?
3. What would you say?
4. You could practise by saying it out loud, somewhere you feel safe
5. Picture how the person might respond if you told them

Think of a way to look after yourself if they respond in a way which isn't what you'd hoped. Remember, the first person you speak to might not be able to help. This may not be their fault – or yours. Don't give up – it does matter that you try again.

What if you can't talk to someone you know?

If there is no one you feel you can trust at the moment, you could try a telephone helpline. They can be very helpful when there's no one else you can turn to. They can make you feel more relaxed and able to speak than you might think – and it's up to you when you finish the conversation.

It's sometimes easier to talk to someone trained to help, who doesn't know you.

There are a lot of places that offer advice and help. You could contact a youth counselling service (Youth Access, can tell you which one is nearest to you).

Your doctor or school nurse should be able to advise you about what support is available locally. They could refer you to someone who has experience of helping people who self-injure.

'What helped was having someone to talk to who was reliable and didn't rush me. I haven't done anything to myself for ages now. Sometimes I feel like it, but I don't need to do it any more, and the feeling goes.'

The person you see will want to help – and won't think you are stupid, mad or wasting their time. The service is confidential (they should explain what this means and also the rare times when they will have to tell someone else) – no one else will know what you've talked about. They are used to talking to people who have all sorts of worries. They can help you work out what's bothering you, even if you're not sure what to say. Although it can take a lot of courage and determination, it's important to keep trying. You will find the right person to help you in the end.

Friends and family – how you can help

'Cutting was always a very secret thing . . . You feel so ashamed, so bad about yourself. You feel no one will ever understand.'

If you are worried about someone who is self-injuring and want to help, this section tells you some things you can do.

Friends and family have a really important part to play. You can help by:

- Noticing that someone is self-injuring
- Offering to listen and support
- Getting help when it's needed

It may be difficult to understand why someone injures themselves. You may feel shocked, angry or even guilty. It can also be hard to know how to help. Here are some suggestions:

- Keep an open mind – don't judge or jump to conclusions
- Make time to listen and take them seriously
- Help them to find their own way of managing their problems
- Help them work out who else can help
- Offer to go with them to tell someone, or offer to tell someone for them
- Carry on with the ordinary activities you do together

- Don't be offended if they don't want to handle things your way
- Don't tease them – respect their feelings
- Support any positive steps they take.

What to do if the situation looks dangerous

'She made me swear I wouldn't tell anyone. I knew if I did she would have hated my guts. On the other hand, if I didn't, she could have died and I would have felt it was my fault. I did tell someone, but she wouldn't speak to me after.'

Someone may tell you that they are hurting themselves and ask you to keep it a secret. This can put you in a very difficult situation.

Of course, it's important to respect their wish for privacy. But

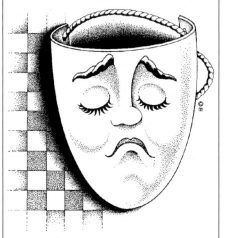

if you think their life is in danger it is important to get help as soon as you can.

You may be able to work out together who would be the best person to tell. If not, try and let

them know that you had to tell someone, and why.

It's important to remember that your feelings matter too . . .
- Look after yourself – make sure you get the support you need
- Remember – even those trained to work with people who self-injure need support, so it's OK if you do too
- Try to carry on with your other activities and relationships
- You don't have to be available for them all the time
- If they hurt themselves it is not because of you, even if they say it is.

• The above is an extract from the Young Minds' web site which can be found at www.youngminds.org.uk

Analysing suicide statistics

The suicide rate is not uniform across the whole population. Important variables are:

Sex and sexual orientation
Suicide is consistently twice as high in men as in women, though parasuicide is greater amongst women. This may owe something to the method used (men typically choose more violent means of death), and the fact that men are often more reluctant to seek help. Lesbian and gay youths are particularly at risk of suicide and a strong sense of isolation is an important contributory factor.

Race
Suicide levels are significantly high in young Asian (especially Indian) women; the rate amongst first-generation immigrants in the 15-24 age range being three times greater than the national average. Research into the issue suggested that racial prejudice was less important than restricting traditional values. However, other studies have emphasised the importance of racism as a contributory factor to depression (also poor socio-economic conditions and prospects).

Unemployment
Research shows a clear link between unemployment rates and the frequency of suicidal behaviour, especially amongst males. This trend is found throughout the European Community; though the link is not straightforward since suicide rates among youths are linked to the general unemployment rate rather than the specific unemployment rate amongst young adults, i.e. unemployment amongst members of the family may be as significant in causing family tensions and depression, as well as unemployment for an individual. A study in Edinburgh published in 1993 found that the unemployed were eleven times more likely to attempt suicide than those in employment.

Suicide is the most common cause of death among young people, with a 50% increase in the number of suicides among men under 25 in the past decade

Occupation
It is known that some occupational groups have a suicide rate which is greater than expected compared to the population as a whole.

Vets represent the highest risk occupation (a suicide rate three and a half times greater than for men as a whole), but numerically farms are more important.

One of the linking factors between the high risk groups for both men and women is that they tend to have easy access to the means of death. Vets, dentists etc. often poison themselves, whilst farmers tend to use firearms. Farmers wives use less violent methods, principally poison or hanging.

Age
The two age groups most at risk of suicide are the young, and elderly people. Suicide is the most common cause of death among young people, with a 50% increase in the number of suicides among men under 25 in the past decade. Young women represent 90% of all cases of non-fatal self-injury. Adolescence is an especially vulnerable time for people and

family breakdowns, difficulties in relationships etc. can precipitate crises. To many adults the cause of the crisis can appear unimportant; but to the teenager it can be the cause of substantial depression and misery. Adolescent warning signs may include truancy, running away, overuse of alcohol and drugs, and risk-taking behaviour. Young people are also caught up within the wider social problems such as unemployment, family breakdowns, alcohol and drug misuse.

Particular concern arises about the elderly because they have a disproportionately high suicide rate (50% higher than the average for the population as a whole) and also because studies show that most parasuicide admissions to hospital of elderly patients were failed suicide attempts. If they try a second time they are likely to succeed. After adolescence, the next greatest time of change that people face is their twilight years. The processes of growing old may precipitate feelings of helplessness and hopelessness, loss of well-being, impaired mobility etc. Bereavement of a loved one is a common factor in many elderly suicide attempts.

Within occupational groups, the age-related incidence of suicide can also be demonstrated. There is particular concern about the disproportionately high incidence of suicide amongst elderly farmers. 11% of all male suicides occur among the post-retirement (65-74 years) age group; whereas 25% of all farmer suicides are from among this age group (163 farmers). The rate for farmers' wives within the post-retirement age range (31% or 45 suicides) is, however, comparable to that for the population of women as a whole (32%).

Depression and psychiatric illness

An individual's 'psychiatric' history is also a contributory factor. For example, if the person has a history of deliberate self-harm the risk of a suicide attempt increases.

Social factors

A common cause of suicide is the break-up of relationships. Recent studies suggest that the highest suicide rates for men aged 15-44 have been found amongst those who were single, divorced or widowed. These men have suicide rates about three times greater than those for married men. Social problems, especially those related to unemployment (see earlier), family stress, relationship problems and social isolation are important factors in assessing suicide risk.

Source unattributable

Suicide and race

Information from MIND

Race and cultural background can be major influences on suicidal behaviour. Patterns of suicide amongst Black and Asian people in the UK are not congruent with patterns of suicide amongst white people. For example, one study of young people of Asian origin in the UK found that the suicide rate of 16-24-year-old women was three times that of 16-24-year-old women of white British origin.[1] This contrasts sharply with the suicide rates of young Asian men who appear to be far less vulnerable to suicide than young men from white British backgrounds. Asian women's groups have linked the high suicide rates amongst young Asian women to cultural pressures: conservative parental values and traditions such as arranged marriages may clash with the wishes and expectations of young women themselves. Highly dangerous suicide methods such as self-burning are more common amongst young Asian women than other groups.[2] Self-burning is a common method of suicide amongst women in India, having its origins in the traditional practice of Hindu widows burning themselves on their husband's funeral pyre – a practice known as 'suttee'.

Little is known about suicide rates amongst Black people in the UK. This is due in part to the fact that British death certificates do not record any details of an individual's racial or cultural identity, unlike the United States where these details are routinely recorded.

One British study of attempted suicides found that young Black women appeared particularly vulnerable to suicide and that suicide attempts amongst young Black people

Little is known about suicide rates amongst Black people in the UK

increased more rapidly than in young white people during the late 1970s.[3]

Recent statistics from the Samaritans suggest that there has been a 22% increase in suicide amongst Irish and Scottish people in recent years.[4]

References
1 Raleigh, V.S. & Balarajan, R. (1992) 'Suicide and Self-Burning among Indians and West Indians in England and Wales' *British Journal of Psychiatry*, 129, 365-368.
2 Raleigh, V.S. & Balarajan, R. (1992) 'Suicide and Self-Burning among Indians and West Indians in England and Wales' *British Journal of Psychiatry*, 129, 365-368.
3 Burke, A.W. (1976) 'Sociocultural Determinants of Attempted Suicide among West Indians in Birmingham: Ethnic Origin and Immigrant Status' *British Journal of Psychiatry*, 161, 261-266.
4 The Samaritans (1998) 'Information Resource Pack'.

Suicide and mental health

What is the relationship between suicide and mental health problems?

The reduction of suicide has been identified by the Government as the measure for targeting mental ill-health.[1] However official suicide statistics are based on coroners' verdicts which are likely to underestimate the true extent of suicide, whereas research on suicide often includes figures for undetermined deaths as well; this is where there is inconclusive evidence about the intent to die.

- In 1996 there were 5,905 suicides in the UK; this equates to approximately 1 suicide every 90 minutes.[2,3] The risk is higher for people who misuse drugs and/or alcohol and who have attempted suicide previously.[4] It is also associated with social deprivation.[5]

Gender differences
- 75% of suicides in the UK are by men.[6]
- The figure for male suicide in the UK rose until 1992 and is now falling.[7] The figure for female suicide is also falling.

Age differences
- Suicide accounts for 20% of all deaths by young people.[8]
- From 1980 to 1990, the suicide rate for men in the UK, between the ages of 15-24, increased by 85%.[9]

- The suicide rate for older people has fallen over the last few decades, although older people are more likely to be successful in their attempts compared with younger people.[10]
- In the UK in 1995, 17% of all suicides were people aged 65 or over.[11]
- The risk is particularly high for males of 45 to 54 years of age, and for females of 75 or over;[11] there is a strong association with depression, physical pain or illness, and living alone.[11]

Ethnic origin
- There has been a 22% increase in suicide for Irish and Scottish people.[12]
- There is a particularly high rate of suicide in South Asian women, particularly young women by burning.[13]

Seasonal differences
- Figures for England and Wales show high levels of suicide in spring and early summer, most notably March, April, May and June.[14] There is also a peak in January.

History of mental health problems
- Suicide is more prevalent amongst people who are known to experience mental health problems or mental illness, compared with the rest of the population.[15]
- 90% of suicide verdicts in England and Wales in 1995 were associated with a 'psychotic disorder'.[16]
- A National Inquiry found that 26% of suicides were by people who had been in contact with mental health services in the last year; 13% of this group were in-patients in a psychiatric hospital at the time of death; 28% had killed themselves within three months of being discharged.[17]
- In young people, 3 in 5 will have experienced 'emotional and behavioural difficulties' for several months prior to the attempt; 1 in 5 will have experienced difficulties for longer.[18]

Schizophrenia
- People with schizophrenia are thought to be at a higher risk of killing themselves.[19,20] An estimated 40% of people with schizophrenia report suicidal thoughts; between 20-40% attempt suicide, and 9-13% end their lives by suicide.[21] The figure is particularly high for people with

long-term schizophrenia at 15%.[22]

- However, recent research suggests that such estimates are influenced by the use of outdated calculation methods and statistics, and that the lifetime risk of suicide for people with schizophrenia is actually about 4%.[23]

Depression

- The lifetime risk of suicide for people with affective disorders such as manic depression and depressive disorders is estimated at 15%.[24] Again the method for calculation of such figures has been criticised; the actual rate may be as low as 6%.[25]
- 70% of recorded suicides are by people who have experienced some form of depression.[26]

Attempted suicide

- Attempted suicide has increased by 50% since 1990.[27]
- The rate for young males has doubled since 1985.[27]
- Young females are most likely to attempt suicide, usually by overdose.[27]
- Young people who have a friend or relative who has harmed or killed themselves are at a great risk of harming themselves.[28]
- A third of adolescents who kill themselves have a history of previous attempts.[29] 1% of people who attempt suicide go on to succeed within a year; this is 100 times the rate for the rest of the population.[30]

References

1 Department of Health. *Our Healthier Nation: A Contract for Health – A Consultation Paper.* The Stationery Office, 1998.

2 Ray, S., Borton, E. & Colyer, I. *Listen Up: Responding to people in crisis.* The Samaritans, 1998.

3 The Samaritans. 'Information Resource Pack.' 1998.

4 Hawton, K., in *Handbook of Affective Disorders.* (2nd ed.) Paykel, E.S. (eds.) Churchill Livingstone, pp 635-650, 1992.

5 Office for National Statistics. 'Geographical variations in suicide mortality 1982-96.' *Population Trends 93.* Autumn 1998.

6 Ray, S., Barton, E. & Colyer, I., *Listen Up: Responding to people in crisis.* The Samaritans 1998.

7 The Samaritans. 'Information Resource Pack.' 1998.

8 The Samaritans. 'Information Resource Pack', 1998. Also: Platt, S., Hawton, K., Kreitman, N., Fagg, J. & Foster, J. 'Recent clinical and epidemiological trends in parasuicide in Edinburgh and Oxford: a tale of two cities.' *Psychological Medicine* (1988) 18:405-18. Gunnell, D.J., Peters, T,J., Kammering, R.M. & Brooks, J. 'Relation between parasuicide, suicide, psychiatric admissions, and socio-economic deprivation.' *British Medical Journal* (1995) 311:226-30.

9 Ray, S., Borton, E. & Colyer, L. *Listen Up: Responding to people in crisis.* The Samaritans, 1998.

10 Katona (1994), in Slater, R. *The Psychology of Growing Old: Looking Forward.* Open University, 1995.

11 The Samaritans. 'Information Resource Pack', 1998.

12 The Samaritans. 'Information Resource Pack' 1998.

13 Soni Raleigh, V. & Balarajan, R. 'Suicide and Self-burning Among Indians and West Indians in England and Wales.' *British Journal of Psychiatry* (1992) 161:365-168.

14 Chew, K.S.Y. & McCleary, R. 'The Spring Peak in Suicide: A Cross-National Analysis.' *Social Science Medicine* (1995) 40:2:223-230.

15 The Audit Commission. *Finding a Place: A Review of Mental Health Services for Adults.* 1994.

16 Department of Health. *National Confidential Inquiry into Suicide and Homicide by People with Mental Illness.* The Stationery Office, 1997.

17 Department of Health. *National Confidential Inquiry into Suicide and Homicide by People with Mental Illness.* The Stationery Office, 1997.

18 Royal College of Psychiatrists. *Suicide and Self-Harm in Young People.* Factsheet 15, for parents and teachers, 1996.

19 Wing, J. & Marshall, P. *Protocol for Visiting Teams: Standards for Clinical & Social Care in Schizophrenia.* Clinical Standards Advisory Group, April 1994.

20 National Schizophrenia Fellowship. *Suicide and Schizophrenia.* NSF, 1993.

21 Meltzer, H.Y. 'Suicide in schizophrenia: risk factors and clozapine treatment.' *Journal of Clinical Psychiatry* (1998) 59: Supplement 3:15-20.

22 Wing, J. & Marshall, P. *Protocol for Visiting Teams: Standards for Clinical & Social Care in Schizophrenia.* Clinical Standards Advisory Group, April 1994.

23 Inskip, H.M., Harris, E.C., Barraclough, B. 'Lifetime risk of suicide for affective disorder, alcoholism and schizophrenia.' *British Journal of Psychiatry* (1998) 172:35-37.

24 Department of Health: Health Advisory Service. *Suicide Prevention: the challenge confronted.* The Stationery Office, 1994.

25 Inskip, H.M., Harris, E.C., Barraclough, B. 'Lifetime risk of suicide for affective disorder, alcoholism and schizophrenia.' *British Journal of Psychiatry* (1998) 172:35-37.

26 Faulkner, A. *Suicide and deliberate self-harm.* Mental Health Foundation, Briefing Paper No. 1. 1997.

27 The Samaritans. 'Information Resource Pack.' 1998.

28 Royal College of Psychiatrists. *Suicide and Self-Harm in Young People.* Factsheet 15, for parents and teachers, 1996.

29 Hawton, K., in *Handbook of Affective Disorders.* (2nd ed.) Paykel, E.S. (eds.) Churchill Livingstone, pp 635-650, 1992.

30 Hawton, K., 'Suicide and attempted suicide,' in *Handbook of Affective Disorders.* (2nd ed.) Paykel, E.S. (eds.) Churchill Livingstone, pp 635-650, 1992.

• The above is an extract from *The Fundamental Facts*, by Bird, L., produced by the Mental Health Foundation. See page 41 for address details.

Causes of suicide

Information from the Mental Health Foundation

There are a number of factors that influence the likelihood of suicide. These include:

- Illness: mental or physical illness, drug or alcohol abuse may have an effect;
- Personal factors: for example, social support and attitude (e.g. religious) towards suicide;
- Stressful life events: e.g. loss of job, bereavement, break-up of marriage, etc.
- Wider cultural environment: e.g. changes in economic climate, cultural attitudes;
- Access to methods: easy access to lethal means.

(Charlton et al, 1993)

The analysis of these different risk factors can add to our understanding of suicide and suicide trends, but there is a limit to the extent to which they can explain or account for changes in an individual's risk of suicide. The likelihood of a person taking his or her own life will depend upon a combination of both risk and protective factors within their own immediate environment. Nevertheless, the analysis of risk factors does provide us with evidence concerning the effects of major changes to the availability of methods. It can also provide ideas about where to target suicide prevention measures.

Mental illness and mental health problems

All forms of mental illness or mental health problems carry an increased risk of suicide, the most common being depression and schizophrenia. The lifetime risk of suicide for people with a diagnosis of schizophrenia has been estimated at between 10 and 15%. For people diagnosed as having affective disorders (mood disorders including manic depression and depression) the lifetime risk of suicide is in the region of 15%. It has been estimated, through the retrospective examination of information about people who have killed themselves, that 70% of recorded suicides are by people suffering from depression.

Depression might be viewed as the 'final common pathway' to suicide, a term coined by Williams and Pollock (1993) in reviewing the psychiatric literature. They found that it is the presence of depressive features in other psychiatric disorders that more reliably predicts suicide. The term is also useful in considering the many other factors associated with suicide; despair or depression may be caused by many life events or circumstances, some of which are covered elsewhere in this information. The importance of demonstrating an association between depression and suicide lies in the opportunity it gives for prevention. The improved detection of depression by primary care professionals, and improvements in treatment and care are all possible routes for suicide prevention.

Mental health factors interact with age and with gender: for example, in people diagnosed with schizophrenia, it is young men who are at the greatest risk of suicide. In relation to depression, community surveys suggest that as many as 16% of older people may be suffering from depression, but that only a fraction of these may be known to the GP and psychiatric services. Depression in older people is treatable, but tends to be overlooked in favour of the care or treatment of physical conditions associated with old age, or dementia.

Alcohol and drug use

Estimates suggest that around 15% of people who abuse alcohol may eventually kill themselves. Alcohol is also often used immediately before or during suicide attempts, thereby increasing the risk of death. The risk

Key facts about suicide

- There were 5,905 recorded suicides in the UK in 1996.
- 140,000 people attempt suicide each year in England and Wales alone.
- Estimates suggest the true suicide rate is 50-60% higher than the official rate.
- 75% of suicides in the UK are by males.
- Suicides in young men aged 15-24 are now 67% higher than in 1982.
- Suicide figures are double the death toll from road traffic accidents.
- The overall UK suicide rate has been slowly declining since the early 1980s.
- Between 1971 and 1996 the suicide rate for women in the UK almost halved.
- Between 1971 and 1996 the suicide rate for men in the UK almost doubled.
- Older men have the highest suicide rates.
- Suicide rates are higher among people with mental health problems.
- Research suggests up to 70% of suicides are by people with depression.
- Drug and alcohol misuse both increase the risk factor for suicide.
- The suicide rate in male prison inmates is six times the male average.
- Overdosing accounts for 50% of female suicides and 25% of male suicides.
- 10-15% of people who make a suicide attempt will later die by suicide.
- Young women 15-19 are at the highest risk of attempted suicide.
- The suicide rate among homeless is 35 times that of the general population.

© MIND

of suicide among people who abuse drugs is also known to be very high, one estimate putting it at 20 times that of the general population. Alcohol and drug problems are common in people who have attempted suicide, and substance abuse is a key risk factor for subsequent suicide following attempted suicide in young people. It is thought that alcohol and drugs play a significant role where impulsiveness is a factor in the decision to act, and are particularly implicated in suicides among young men.

Physical illness

People with a chronic physical illness are at greater risk of suicide, very probably because of the high rate of depression among people with a chronic physical illness. Diseases which have been found to be associated with high suicide rates are: neurological, gastrointestinal, cardiovascular and malignant disorders, and HIV and AIDS. Prevention of suicide in this case is thought to be best targeted at the training of medical staff in the detection and management of depression, although it seems likely that improvements in the care and treatment of the underlying illness would also make an important contribution.

Occupation

Figures on occupation are traditionally analysed using men's death certificates, since occupation has not been recorded routinely on women's death certificates. Nevertheless, the data suggest that certain occupations have a higher risk of suicide associated with them than others. These include veterinary surgeons, pharmacists, dentists, farmers and doctors. Suicide in veterinary surgeons is around 3 times more common than in the general population and in pharmacists, dentists, farmers and doctors it is around twice as common. Many of these are occupations which provide easy access to both the methods and knowledge about the methods of suicide. Also these occupations may be particularly prone to stress and, in the case of farmers, to financial difficulties and isolation.

Unemployment

Although the rate of suicide is higher among unemployed people than among employed people, the association is not a straightforward one. In the 1981-1990 period, male suicide rates were highest at the time when unemployment rates were lowest. However the effect of unemployment on an individual may be greater when national unemployment rates are low, and may also be influenced by the realistic chance of finding alternative employment. Analysis of mortality in the years following the 1971 and 1981 Censuses found that men who were unemployed and seeking work at the time of census were 2-3 times more likely to kill themselves than the general population. However numbers were small and accounted for only a small proportion of all suicides.

Marital breakdown

Patterns of suicide associated with marital breakdown are different in men and women, suggesting that marriage may act as more of a protective factor for men than it does for women. Until recently, widowed and divorced people of both sexes generally had a higher rate of suicide than single or married men and women. The rate for single men has in recent years become higher than the rates for widowed and divorced women. Widowed and divorced men have the highest rates of suicide, about twice the rate for women in the same situation.

Evidence from studies looking at the mental health of men and women have concluded that marriage 'benefits' men more than it does women. It is married women and single men who are at the greatest risk of mental health problems (Ussher, 1991). Charlton et al (1993) suggest that the increased proportion of single and divorced men in the younger age categories goes some way towards explaining the increased suicide rate in young men.

Young Asian women

There is consistent evidence of high suicide rates among certain sub-groups of young Asian women, particularly those of Hindu or Sikh origin. It is thought that this reflects the raised suicide rates among young women resident in India and in other countries where people from the Indian sub-continent have settled (Soni Raleigh & Balarajan, 1992). However, it does indicate a need to investigate the suicide rates and causes among people of minority ethnic communities in this country, an analysis made difficult by the fact that ethnic origin is not recorded routinely at death registration.

Lesbians and gay men

Research carried out in the United States suggests that suicide rates for young lesbians and gay men may be considerably higher than rates for young heterosexual men and women. A report commissioned by the US Government concluded that lesbian

and gay youths were 2 or 3 times more likely to attempt suicide than other young people, and that they may account for 30% of suicides in young people. The London Gay Teenage Project (1984) found that 19% of their sample of 415 respondents had attempted suicide. Other US studies have suggested as many as 40-50% of young lesbians and gay men have attempted suicide. In comparison, the Samaritans North London Youth Project found that around 11% of a large sample of 13-17-year-olds had at some time attempted suicide. Age is an important factor for lesbians and gay men, since young people who are in the process of coming to terms with their sexuality are particularly vulnerable to isolation and stigma among their friends and families.

People in prison and on probation

The number of recorded suicides in prisons has risen from around 15 per year in 1961 to around 40 per year in 1988-90 (although it should be noted that the prison population has also risen considerably in the same period). In 1994 the figure rose to an unprecedented 61 deaths by suicide, a 30% increase over the number of suicides in 1993 (The Howard League for Penal Reform, 1995). All but one of these were men and over half were under the age of 30. More than 40% were prisoners on remand. Possible explanations for the rise in prison suicides include the increase in the proportion of remand prisoners, overcrowding, and less supervision and support. Prisoners are also likely to be vulnerable to other risk factors for suicide: previous psychiatric history, self-harm, alcohol or drug abuse, social isolation and marital disruption. One study ascribes 40% of prison suicides to the prison environment, 15% to outside pressures, 12% to guilt feelings and 22% to diagnosed severe mental illness (Dooley, cited in the Department of Health publication *The Prevention of Suicide*, 1994).

A recent study in West Yorkshire (Akhurst et al, 1994) found a very high incidence of deliberate self-harm among offenders supervised by the Probation Service. Almost

---

Suicide in older people

Although suicide rates in older people of both sexes have dropped considerably since the 1950s, they are still high, with older men showing the highest rates. Suicide in older people is strongly associated with depression, physical pain or illness, living alone and feelings of hopelessness and guilt. Community surveys suggest that as many as 16% of older people may be experiencing depression, but that only a fraction of these may be known to GP and psychiatric services.

Most suicides in older people occur in the community, and most have had no contact with old age psychiatry services. Cattell & Jolley's recent research found that community old age psychiatry services were seeing less than 25% of older people with depression who later went on to kill themselves, and most of these people had not seen their family doctor within the month prior to suicide.[1]

The most common means of suicide in older people are overdose of prescribed and over-the-counter drugs and hanging, the latter being far more frequent in older men.

Reference
1   Cattell, H. & Jolley, D.J. 'One Hundred Cases of Suicide in Elderly People.' *British Journal of Psychiatry* (1995) 166: 451-457.

© MIND

---

one-third of the 238 people involved reported one or more incidents of self-harm, 72% of which were believed to be serious attempts at suicide. The profile of offenders was observed to be very similar to the profile of factors commonly associated with suicide and self-harm: high levels of unemployment, alcohol and drug misuse, breakdown in family relations and mental health problems.

Homelessness

Homelessness greatly increases the likelihood of a suicide attempt. In a recent study of young homeless people (Craig et al, 1996), one-fifth of the sample had attempted suicide in the last year compared to 4% of a group of non-homeless young people. One-third of the homeless group had attempted suicide at some point in their lives. Self-poisoning was the most common method. There was a strong association between suicide attempts and psychiatric diagnosis: 29% of those who attempted suicide were diagnosed as having a mental illness and 19% were substance abusers.

References
Akhurst, M., Brown, I. & Wessely, S. *Dying for Help: Offenders at risk of suicide*. West Yorkshire Probation Service, West Yorkshire Health Authority, Association of Chief Officers of Probation; 1994.

Charlton, J. et al. 'Suicide Deaths in England and Wales: Trends in factors associated with suicide deaths.' *Population Trends* No.71, 34-42. ONS, HMSO; 1993.

Craig, T.K.J. et al. *Off to a Bad Start: A longitudinal study of homeless young people in London*. The Mental Health Foundation, 1996.

Department of Health. *The Health of the Nation*. Cm 1986; HMSO, 1992.

Department of Health. *The Prevention of Suicide*. Edited by Jenkins, R. et al. HMSO, 1994.

London Gay Teenage Project. *Something to Tell You*. 1984.

Soni Raleigh, V. and Balarajan, R. 'Suicide and Self-Burning among Indians and West Indians in England and Wales.' *British Journal of Psychiatry* (1992), 161, 365-368.

Ussher, J. *Women's Madness*. Harvester Wheatsheaf, 1991.

Williams, J.M.G. & Pollock, L.R. 'Factors mediating suicidal behaviour: Their utility in primary and secondary prevention.' *Journal of Mental Health* (1993) 2, 3-26.

• The above information is an extract from *Suicide and deliberate self-harm*, a Mental Health Foundation Briefing. See page 41 for address details.

© Mental Health Foundation

Suicide in prisons

Information from MIND

In 1997 there were 70 suicides in prisons in England and Wales, 67 men and 3 women. This is a 40% increase since 1990 and a huge 159% increase since 1983. This rate translates as being over six times the total male suicide rate. 39% of those who committed suicide were on remand.

Liebling and Krarup conducted the most comprehensive study ever into suicide and self-harm in prison between 1990 and 1992. Their research report, published in 1993, identified a range of characteristics and background factors associated with prisoners at risk of suicide and self-harm.[1] They found that many prisoners had experienced multiple deprivations prior to their imprisonment, and to this was added the stresses resulting from custody and a range of situational problems. Although all prisoners may be vulnerable at certain times, they found that there were three particularly vulnerable groups: younger 'poor copers', those with mental health problems and serious adult male offenders.

Within the prison population as a whole, young prisoners are the individuals most at risk, particularly those under 21 who make up a third of the remand population. In 1995, 20% of prison suicides were by people under 21, the vast majority being young males.[2]

Liebling and Krarup found that mental health problems were present in approximately one-third of prison suicides, however, their research suggests that coping problems and situational factors are more significant than psychiatric explanations.

Judge Tumin, then Chief Inspector of Prisons, was commissioned by the Home Secretary to carry out a review of the Prison Service's policy on suicide and self-harm. This report was published in 1990, and in it Judge Tumin stated: 'Current Prison Service policy fails to communicate the social dimension to self-harm and self-inflicted death. It does not stress sufficiently the significance of the environment in which prisoners and staff are expected to live and work, or the importance of constructive activities in helping inmates to cope with anxiety and stress. Above all, it fails to give weight to the need to sustain people during their time of custody, the importance of relationships between inmates and between staff and inmates in providing support.'[3]

This research and review has led to the Prison Service developing a new policy called 'Caring for the

> *Within the prison population as a whole, young prisoners are the individuals most at risk, particularly those under 21*

Suicidal in Custody'.[4] The key elements of the policy are:

- Primary care – creating a safe environment and helping prisoners to cope with custody.
- Special care – identifying and supporting the prisoners in crisis and treating them with dignity.
- Aftercare – caring for the needs of those affected by suicide and self-harm
- Community responsibility – involving the whole prison community in the awareness and care of the suicidal.

References
1 Liebling, A. & Krarup, H. (1992) Institute of Criminology, Cambridge University.
2 Samaritans. *Exploring The Taboo* (1998).
3 HM Chief Inspector of Prisons (1990) Review of Suicide and Self-Harm.
4 HM Prison Service (1994) *Caring for the Suicidal in Custody – Principles of Prison Service Policy.*

© MIND

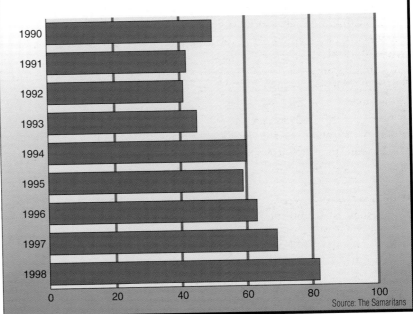

Self-inflicted deaths in prison

In 1998 there were 82 self-inflicted deaths in prisons in England and Wales, 79 were male and 3 female. This represents a 17% on the previous year and a 64% increase since 1990.

Source: The Samaritans

Jail suicide rate doubles in 15 years

By Ian Burrell, Home Affairs Correspondent

More than a thousand prisoners – at least one in 60 of the jail population – is a suicide risk, the director-general of the Prison Service said yesterday.

Martin Narey said the 'dreadful' suicide rate among prisoners had doubled from 62 per 100,000 in 1983 to 125 per 100,000 last year.

Mr Narey, who was appointed director-general eight weeks ago, said that there was now an action plan aimed at reversing the growing death toll.

The announcement comes ahead of a report on prison suicide to be published this week by Sir David Ramsbotham, the Chief Inspector of Prisons, which is expected to be critical.

Mr Narey pledged to eliminate the use of strip cells for vulnerable prisoners by April 2000. Such bare rooms had been regarded as the safest environment for suicidal inmates.

Instead, high-risk prisoners will be placed in private 'comfortable suites' where meals are taken, which can have three separate rooms equipped with armchairs, television and private showers.

Prisoners will be kept under 24-hour supervision by closed-circuit television. The policy is a significant change from the days when mentally unsettled inmates – callously dubbed 'fraggles' by fellow inmates – were slung into a 'strip cell' for their own safety.

All prisons will be expected to have a number of 'safe cells', designed with no ligature points so that inmates cannot hang themselves.

The cells have no handles on the window-frames and no heating pipes. Taps on the sink have been replaced by push buttons.

Even the space under the bed has been filled in after prisoners managed to strangle themselves in the few inches beneath the bedsprings. The new design will be used for all future prison cell-blocks.

Suicidal inmates will also be encouraged to take part in arts-related therapies, including painting and drama. Prison chiefs are encouraged by the results of a sound and light therapy project, pioneered at Belmarsh high-security prison in south London.

Vulnerable prisoners are relaxed by soothing music as they sit in a room where kaleidoscopic colours are projected on to walls and bounced off a disco-style glitter ball that hangs from the ceiling.

Mr Narey has also been impressed by work at the notorious Ryker's Island jail in New York, where suicides have been greatly reduced after staff were trained to recognise mental illness. The director-general wants similar training in England and Wales.

'The old philosophy of using strip cells was inhuman,' he said. 'The move has to be away from that treatment to an approach which is rather more supportive to the individual.'

Mr Narey said the bulk of prison admissions were young men from deprived backgrounds, often with psychiatric or drug problems. He intends to meet the families of prisoners who died in custody and let them see internal reports on the deaths.

© The Independent, May, 1999

Steep rise in suicides worries jail reformers

By Libby Brooks

The steep increase in prison suicides can be reversed only by cutting the use of custodial sentences, a report by the Howard League penal reform group said yesterday.

More and more vulnerable people were receiving prison terms – many with a history of drug and alcohol addiction, family break-up or psychiatric disorders – who could be more effectively dealt with by probation or community sentences, the report said.

The number of prisoners committing suicide rose from 37 in 1988 to an unprecedented 82 last year; the figure so far this year is 42. There were 126 suicides per 100,000 prisoners last year, compared with 12 per 100,000 in the population as a whole.

The report said the isolation and boredom of prison life often made the situation unbearable for vulnerable inmates.

The rising prison population, from 50,000 in 1988 to more than 65,300 last year, had compounded the problem. Pressure on resources had left many inmates spending more time in overcrowded cells.

The problems were most acute among prisoners on remand, who accounted for 54% of suicides since 1990. Conditions for these prisoners were often among the worst, because they were held in the most overcrowded jails and sometimes spent 23 hours a day in their cells.

Two in five women and one in five men in prison had previously attempted suicide, according to figures released by the Office of National Statistics yesterday.

Those most likely to have tried to kill themselves were young, white and single, had left school early and were poorly educated.

Frances Crook, director of the Howard League, said: 'We believe that a sea change in prison culture and standards is needed to deal with this problem.'

© The Guardian, July, 1999

Copycat suicides and media reporting

Information from The Samaritans

The evidence

Concern over how individual suicides are reported in the media has arisen from studies which have indicated a risk of copycat suicides, particularly amongst adolescents and young adults. There is a general agreement that reporting suicide is important and can be beneficial. There is more dissent over the nature of the coverage given to the subject.

Copycat suicides: The case for

Suicide by imitation has long been recognised as a phenomenon. In the US, well-publicised clusters of youth suicide appear to have occurred. The decision to complete a suicide is often an ambiguous one in the mind of the contemplator of it. We know many of the risk factors which make young people vulnerable. The concern is that certain types of media reporting can act as a catalyst.

There is evidence that excessive publicity of actual suicide does increase copycat suicides. For example, in the 1970s, during the 12 months following international publicity of a suicide from burning, there were 60 more suicides from burning in Britain than would normally be expected.

In Australia, research has suggested that more Australian men took their lives immediately after news stories about suicides in the country's two metropolitan newspapers, *The Age* in Melbourne, and the *Sydney Morning Herald*.

Copycat suicides: The case against

It is reasonable to assert that in the case of a completed suicide which coincides with a high-profile media reporting of a suicide, there is rarely evidence that the person saw the coverage. Other factors also need to be taken into account.

There has been less attention to possible media effects in non-fatal suicidal behaviour. A recent analysis of attempted suicides following an episode of *Casualty* (BBC) where a 15-year-old girl took an overdose found no evidence that it had any apparent influence on the people who subsequently took overdoses.

In fact, there was a suggestion that the programme had a positive benefit in that one of the patients in the study had learned through the programme of the possible lethal effects of paracetamol. It is also possible that the effect was not seen because of the sensitive portrayal of the subject.

Also in the drama field, an extensive study undertaken after Angie Watts' suicide attempt on *Eastenders* (BBC) in 1986 did not lend support to the claim that there was a strong imitation effect after this televised attempted suicide. However, there was some evidence within the research to note an effect, and considerable debate within the medical press at the time about the effects. It is possible that the programme brought forward overdoses that may have happened anyway.

There has been little UK research undertaken about the effect of factual reporting of suicide in the media, or about the relationship between reporting of suicides in high-profile locations (e.g. Beachy Head) and subsequent imitative behaviour.

> **There is evidence that excessive publicity of actual suicide does increase copycat suicides**

A positive example

One study into suicide on the Viennese underground system associated dramatic reporting of such suicides with a rise in the subsequent number of suicides taking place on the underground: 13 suicides occurred on the system in 1986 and nine in the first nine months of 1987, there having been only nine suicides between 1983 and 1984. The local media discussed and agreed voluntary reporting guidelines limiting dramatic or sensational coverage given to suicides. For example in 1988 no subway suicide was mentioned in the press. The subsequent number of suicides on the underground fell (four in 1989 and three in 1990) as did the number of attempted suicides on the system.

Conclusions?

There is conflicting evidence on the effect of the media's treatment of suicide on suicide rates in the overall population, but experts do feel that an effect exists, particularly in individual cases, and the young are especially susceptible.

Although the evidence is conflicting, and in many cases lacking, there is cause for concern that inappropriate depiction of suicide can influence the attitudes and behaviour of the audience.

Equally, it is clear that positive explanation of the issue in a sensitive way can help to educate and destigmatise the issue of suicide.

Suicide is a legitimate topic for serious discussion in the media, like other mental health issues. However, the presentation of it should only be done with great care.

• The above information is from The Samaritans. See page 41 for address details.

© *The Samaritans*

Helping distressed young people

Attempted suicide and self-harm

The most common means used in attempted suicide involves overdosing. A parent or carer faced with such a situation has many different tasks to deal with. It may not be clear whether the teenager is going to survive or not, and thus panic, shock and disbelief may all be present. Obviously much depends on the circumstances, but the most likely situation is that the young person will be taken – either by ambulance or by car – to the nearest Accident and Emergency Department. Each year about 44,000 young people under 25 reach hospital in the UK having injured or poisoned themselves. Here a medical assessment will be carried out, and whatever medical treatment is necessary will be undertaken – such as stitching up a wound, or pumping out the stomach, or assessing damage to the liver if the young person has taken paracetamol.

Many parents/carers at this point will want to take the young person home. However, if at all possible a psychological assessment should be carried out by a trained mental health professional. Although this may involve a wait in hospital, a thorough assessment of the teenager's emotional state is critical at this stage. There are a number of reasons for this. First, the parents themselves may be feeling shocked and confused. Because of this they are not the best people to try and understand the young person's distress at this point. Indeed the parents too will need the opportunity of talking to a trained professional about their feelings and reactions.

Second, a major fear will centre around whether the teenager is likely to make a further attempt on his or her life. An assessment by a mental health professional should provide some guidance for the family, but it will also indicate to the young person that his or her problems are being taken seriously.

Research shows that approximately 10% of those who make a suicide attempt will do so again within the next 12 months. Most important, however, is the finding that those who do make a further attempt are those who feel that no real attention has been paid to their distress. In other words those who do it again are those who feel that no one has listened to them.

It is important to recognise also that parents may feel extremely angry with the teenager, particularly once it is established that he or she is not going to die. Parents have all sorts of reactions. How could he or she be so stupid? She's just doing this to get at me! She's just being hysterical/manipulative/attention seeking. All these feelings are entirely normal. After all, suicide and attempted suicide do have strong elements of aggression in them. As one mother put it: 'He was very, very angry, and in a way I feel as if he couldn't kill everyone

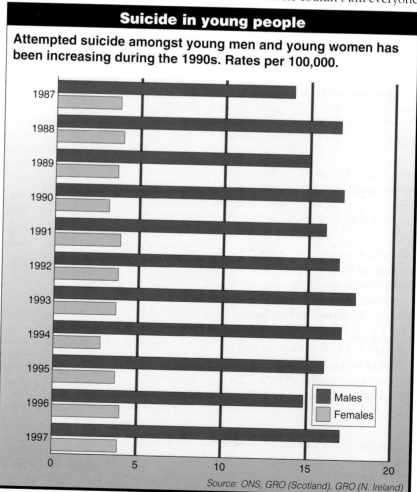

Suicide in young people

Attempted suicide amongst young men and young women has been increasing during the 1990s. Rates per 100,000.

Source: ONS, GRO (Scotland), GRO (N. Ireland)

else, so he killed himself. But he'd have loved to have killed everyone else.'

Recognising the anger that is around – both the teenager's anger and the parents' anger – is an important part of the process of coming to terms with the young person's suicidal behaviour.

What of the long term? It is certainly true that, following an attempted suicide, relationships within the family are never the same again. The young woman who took an overdose in school made this clear when she described the effect on her family: 'It has just caused so many problems at home. Your life has to change totally. They can't trust you with nothing no more. You're like padded in cotton all the time. They're always with you, they won't let you out on your own. It's caused so many problems.'

Inevitably perhaps there will always be the fear that the young person will do it again, and this can lead to overprotective behaviour on the part of the parents. While such behaviour may be understandable, it is likely to create many additional problems. As we have indicated, attempted suicide is a communication – a message if you like – from someone who cannot express their distress in any other way.

After a suicide attempt the situation in the family will improve only if the young person has a real sense that he or she is being taken seriously. If the teenager's worries, fears or depression are dismissed or brushed aside, then there will be little change. Of course there are likely to be communication patterns within the family which are long standing, and difficult to alter. We cannot expect, therefore, that after a suicide attempt everyone will suddenly be able to talk to each other honestly and openly. However, there are many ways in which parents and carers can make sure that the needs of the young person are met in an appropriate and sensitive manner.

Support for young people

As we have said, it is terribly hard to talk about suicide. Fears of saying or doing the wrong thing, fears of making the situation worse, can make it feel impossible for a parent to help at all. Yet parents and carers can help. A suicide attempt may have been made on impulse. Strong suicidal feelings rarely last for very long periods of time. An adult can understand that, but for a distressed teenager it is hard to see ahead, to imagine a time when things could be all right again. It will help if parents can find ways gently to support their teenager to get things back in perspective and to develop some sense of having a future. Young people in distress can be helped to realise that they are loved, that they are connected and that their death would hurt those who care about them. One mother said: 'The things I regret so bitterly are of not saying things more directly. "Don't commit suicide." I never said, "Don't kill yourself." I sort of felt I mustn't tell him that. But I should have said, "Look, you know if you kill yourself it will be terrible for us." I never said that. I never said anything that might give him the idea that I cared enough.'

Many adults who spoke had had frustrating experiences. They wanted to help young people in distress, but felt baffled about how to do so. For parents and carers, as well as for professionals, communication difficulties with adolescents can be puzzling and irritating. However the situation can be improved if adults take a step backwards, and try and understand something of what it is like to be a teenager.

Firstly, young people, particularly those who have emotional problems, have very mixed feelings about their parents. While on the one hand they need to be valued and supported by their parents, on the other hand they will be keen to show that they are not dependent. However troubled and upset young people may feel, they do not want to be seen as or treated like children. Secondly, it is very important for adolescents, especially in the early years, to maintain a certain amount of privacy. Most young people do not wish their parents to know about their inner world. Thus to be asked to share fears and worries can seem like an invasion of a private space. Thirdly, teenagers often say that adults talk at them, rather than with them. Rarely do teenagers feel that the adults around them are really listening to their side of the story. More commonly adults appear keen to get their points across, rather than to have a genuine dialogue.

Effective communication has to take these issues into account. Clearly it is no use saying to a young person, 'Right. Sit down. I want to talk about your problems now.' Yet this is often the way that adults appear to teenagers. Young people in distress do need help from adults, but that help can only be accepted if a number of fairly basic rules are observed.

- Communication is more likely if it focuses on the young person's agenda, rather than the adults' agenda.
- Communication has to involve active listening as well as talking.
- Communication will be more successful if it takes place at a time or in a place chosen by the young person.
- For a variety of reasons the young person may find communication with a parent very difficult. If this is the case the parent should support the young person in identifying another adult who may be able to help. In the short term, telephone helpline counsellors may have an important role to play.
- Communication does not necessarily involve talking or listening. Simply to indicate to the teenager that you are available, if and when you are needed, is a very powerful message.
- Finally, adolescents may feel ashamed, guilty or confused by their problem. Try and make allowances for the fact that young people will not articulate what the problem is. Sympathy and patience on the part of the adult will make communication easier.

- The above is an extract from *Teenage Suicide and Self-Harm*, a multi-media pack produced by the Trust for the Study of Adolescence. See page 41 for address details.

© *Trust for the Study of Adolescence*

How do I know if someone close to me is suicidal?

Information from MIND

Warning signs

Even though suicidal feelings often develop gradually, others may not be aware of them because they are not easy to talk about in a direct way. Someone who is suicidal may find it hard to share these forbidden feelings and therefore disguise them. Suicide may appear to happen 'out of the blue' and family and friends may feel mystified about why someone has taken their own life.

Warning signs that someone is feeling suicidal vary from one individual to another, but may include some of the following:

- A marked change in the person's behaviour. Someone may appear to be calm and at peace for the first time or, more usually, may be withdrawn and have difficulties in communicating.
- Expressing feelings of failure, loss of self-esteem, isolation and loss of hope.
- People may express feelings of uselessness and ask, 'What's the point?'
- Talking about suicide. It is a myth that people who talk about suicide don't do it. In fact, studies show that most people who have taken their own lives have spoken of it to someone.

There is a particular risk of suicide when someone who has been suffering from depression is just beginning to recover. They may have the energy to kill themselves which they lacked when they were severely depressed.

Don't people have a right to kill themselves if they want to?

Some people make repeated suicide attempts and appear to express a strong, unambivalent wish for death. One carer's reaction on being told of her son's death was, 'Thank goodness for that'. Family and friends may come to accept that death is the inevitable outcome of so much emotional anguish. They may feel relieved that the person will not have to face further suffering.

However, many people are far more ambivalent, and suicidal feelings may come and go according to the stresses and strains in their day-to-day lives. For many people there are likely to be less extreme ways of resolving problems. Even when someone appears to be absolutely determined to take their own life, the importance of talking and examining every possible option and source of support cannot be overestimated. It is important to encourage the person not to view suicide as the only possible solution.

How can I help someone who feels that bad?

The two chief concerns which you are likely to have if you are trying to help someone who is suicidal are about their immediate safety and the causes of their desperation. It is important to encourage the person to talk about their despairing feelings and not to dismiss expressions of hopelessness as a 'cry for help' or try to jolly them out of it. Talking openly about the possibility of suicide will not make it more likely to happen.

Just being there for the person and listening in an accepting way could contribute to making them feel less isolated and frightened.

At the same time, if you are in a close relationship with them you are likely to feel fearful, angry or guilty. You will need to find someone –

whether a friend, family member, a professional, the Samaritans, or a carers' support group – in whom you can confide your fears. It is also important to persuade the suicidal person to get some outside support.

The GP is a good starting-point for professional help and may be able to arrange for other help such as counselling to be made available or to prescribe anti-depressants if appropriate.

It may be useful to emphasise to the suicidal person that overdosing with certain drugs will not be an easy answer to all their problems. Overdosing can lead to messy, painful and long-drawn-out consequences such as slow poisoning.

It is important to discuss strategies for seeking help when suicidal thoughts occur. Creating a personal support list is a useful way of reviewing every conceivable option. The list may include the names, phone numbers and addresses of

It is important to encourage the person to talk about their despairing feelings and not to dismiss expressions of hopelessness as a 'cry for help'

individuals, helplines, organisations and professionals available to someone should they need support. Persuade the person to keep this list by the phone and to agree to call someone on the list when they are feeling suicidal.

For a young person who has expressed suicidal feelings, drawing up such a list is in itself a sign of care and concern. Often young people may resist sharing their personal feelings and problems. If they are reluctant to seek outside help, the

information may provide food for thought, allowing them the option of seeking help when they feel ready. Do not neglect yourself: you should compile your own list to ensure that your needs for support and advice are met.

Surviving or diffusing a suicidal crisis is one thing, solving underlying problems another. The difficulties that nurture despair are usually complex and do not vanish quickly. It is essential to address these underlying problems or suicidal feelings may well return. Seeking help with the problems that have led to suicidal unhappiness will represent the starting-point of a lengthy process.

• The above is an extract from *HOW TO . . . help someone who is suicidal*, by permission of MIND (National Association for Mental Health). See page 41 for address details.
© MIND (National Association for Mental Health)

Not just a 'cry for help'

Information from PAPYRUS

This information is for you if you know someone who has made a suicide attempt.

It gives some guidance on how you can help him or her through this crisis, and offers some information about organisations that can *help you to help them*.

Knowing that someone we care about is feeling suicidal can be emotionally and physically draining. It is important to look after your own health and to make time to get support and advice for yourself too.

You are not alone

Attempted suicide is far more common than most of us realise. In England and Wales, more than 140,000 people are admitted to accident and emergency departments each year because they have tried to kill themselves.

Although most people who attempt suicide survive, a few remain

at high risk of taking their own life for quite some time afterwards. This means that **any** suicide attempt, however minor it seems to be, should be taken seriously.

Why did it happen?
Thinking about suicide
Suicidal thoughts can coincide with times of change – whether these changes are 'good' (like getting married or starting a new job), or 'bad' (such as someone dying or the end of a relationship).

Quite often two or three different things will have happened, each of them causing considerable stress.

For some people there may be no apparent reason for these thoughts.

The circumstances leading up to a suicide attempt are different for everybody, and the reasons for it happening may never be fully explained or understood.

Often those who think about suicide are depressed. Usually very sensitive people, they may have been in despair, feeling hopeless about the future and unable to think straight. Everyday worries have become totally out of proportion, and black thoughts may have left no room for anyone or anything else.

Acting on the thought
Turning thoughts about suicide into action is sometimes done on impulse, perhaps following an event that is seen as 'the last straw'. This is especially true of young people.

Others however may have been making plans about suicide for some time.

Using alcohol and/or other drugs can make things worse. They take away the inhibitions which would otherwise stop someone from attempting to take their own life.

It's hard to talk . . .
about fears and feelings – even to those we know love and care about us. This can prevent other people from recognising the distress and being able to help in a crisis.

Words are often totally inadequate to convey the amount of pain a person may be suffering.

It is easy to understand that someone is hurting if they have been badly injured or are physically ill. Emotional pain cannot be seen, but it can be just as unbearable.

Sometimes attempting suicide may be the only way to show other people how bad things are.

'When your back is up against the wall, suicide can seem to be the only way out.'

What can be done to help?
Do keep 'Alert'

Ask them *how they were feeling before it happened and how they are feeling now.* Talking about suicide does not make it more likely to happen. Try to be patient if they are angry or refuse to talk. It may be that writing things down is an easier way for them to communicate with you.

Listen – **this is the most important thing you can do**. Treat them with respect, and try not to be judgemental or critical.

Empathise by showing that *you really are trying to understand* things from their point of view. Words don't always matter. The touch of a hand or a hug can go a long way to show that you care.

Reassure *them* that desperate feelings are very common and can be overcome. Things can and do change, help can be found and there is hope for the future. People **do** get better!

Try *to give practical support*, and help them to cope with any extra pressures. It may not be possible to deal with all the things that are troubling them, but between you agree on what you will do if a suicidal crisis happens again.

And don't
Put *them down* or do things that might make them feel worse. A suicide attempt suggests that self-esteem is already very low.

Abandon *or reject* them in any way. Your help, support and attention are vital if they are to begin to feel that life is worth living again. Don't relax your attentions just because they seem to be better. It doesn't mean that life is back to normal for them yet. They may be at risk for quite a while.

Nag – although it may be well meant. Nobody wants to be pestered all the time. Don't intrude – try to balance being watchful with a respect for privacy.

Ignore what has happened.

Criticise their actions – however you may be feeling about their suicide attempt, try to remember the pain and turmoil that they were, and may still be, going through. Don't take their behaviour personally – it was not necessarily directed at you.

Help from services
There are many ways in which health workers, social services staff and others can help someone who has attempted suicide. The staff in the hospital accident and emergency department may make a referral, or the family doctor can be asked to.

Treating depression: suicidal feelings may be linked to being depressed. Depression is a serious illness but can be successfully treated by antidepressant medication and/or 'talking and listening' treatments. Further information about depression and its treatment can be obtained from Depression Alliance, 35 Westminster Bridge Road, London SE1 7JB (020 7633 9929).

Extra help in a crisis
If you feel that the situation is getting worse rather than better, and you are worried about another suicide attempt, trust your instinct and share your concerns straight away. Contact the family doctor, or any professional who has been involved already.

These people cannot discuss confidential details with you, **but they will want to listen to what you are saying and they <u>can</u> follow it up**.

Further information and help
PAPYRUS can send you a list of useful contacts and literature.
Phone: 01706 214449
Or e-mail: papyrus_uk@hotmail.com

Befrienders International

Working to prevent suicide worldwide with 31,000 volunteers in over 40 countries

Helping a suicidal friend or relative

Be quiet and listen!

If someone is feeling depressed or suicidal, our first response is to try to help. We offer advice, share our own experiences, try to find solutions.

We'd do better to be quiet and listen. People who feel suicidal don't want answers or solutions. They want a safe place to express their fears and anxieties, to be themselves.

Listening – really listening – is not easy. We must control the urge to say something – to make a comment, add to a story or offer advice. We need to listen not just to the facts that the person is telling us but to the feelings that lie behind them. We need to understand things from their perspective, not ours.

Here are some points to remember if you are helping a person who feels suicidal.

What do people who feel suicidal want?

- Someone to listen. Someone who will take time to really listen to them. Someone who won't judge, or give advice or opinions, but will give their undivided attention.
- Someone to trust. Someone who will respect them and won't try to take charge. Someone who will treat everything in complete confidence.
- Someone to care. Someone who will make themselves available, put the person at ease and speak calmly. Someone who will re-assure, accept and believe. Someone who will say, 'I care.'

What do people who feel suicidal not want?

To be alone

Rejection can make the problem seem ten times worse. Having someone to turn to makes all the difference.

Listen.

To be advised

Lectures don't help. Nor does a

suggestion to 'cheer up', or an easy assurance that 'everything will be okay'. Don't analyse, compare, categorise or criticise.

Listen.

To be interrogated

Don't change the subject, don't pity or patronise. Talking about feelings is difficult. People who feel suicidal don't want to be rushed or put on the defensive.

Listen.

When someone feels suicidal

We are born with the ability to take our own lives. Each year a million people make that choice. Even in societies where suicide is illegal or taboo, people still kill themselves.

For many people who feel suicidal, there seems to be no other way out. Death describes their world at that moment and the strength of their suicidal feelings should not be underestimated – they are real and powerful and immediate. There are no magic cures.

But it is also true that

- Suicide is often a permanent solution to a temporary problem.
- When we are depressed, we tend to see things through the very narrow perspective of the present moment. A week or a month later, things may look completely different.
- Most people who once thought about killing themselves are now glad to be alive. They say they didn't want to end their lives – they just wanted to stop the pain.

The most important step is to talk to someone. People who feel suicidal should not try to cope alone. They should seek help NOW.

- Talk to family or friends. Just talking to a family member or a friend or a colleague can bring huge relief.
- Talk to a befriender. Some people cannot talk to family or friends. Some find it easier to talk to a stranger. There are befriending centres all over the world, with volunteers who have been trained to listen. If calling is too difficult, the person can send an email.
- Talk to a doctor. If someone is going through a longer period of feeling low or suicidal, he or she may be suffering from clinical depression. This is a medical condition caused by a chemical imbalance, and can usually be treated by a doctor through the prescription of drugs and/or a referral to therapy.

Time is an important factor in 'moving on', but what happens in that time also matters. When someone is feeling suicidal, they should talk about their feelings immediately.

• The above is an extract from the Befrienders International web site which can be found at www.befrienders.org

© 2000 by Befrienders International

Working together for the prevention of young suicide

What is PAPYRUS?

PAPYRUS is a voluntary organisation committed to the prevention of young suicide and the promotion of mental health and well-being. It was founded in 1997 by parents who had lost a son or daughter to suicide.

PAPYRUS is:

Promoting public awareness

Members attend conferences both as delegates and speakers. Many leading newspapers and periodicals have chosen to feature PAPYRUS in articles about young suicide. We have taken part in radio and TV programmes, and regularly assist researchers working in the media.

Co-operating, as an organisation, with professional and voluntary bodies working in the suicide prevention field

PAPYRUS is represented on several health committees with some members working as volunteers on mental health help lines.

Encouraging and/or taking part in research into suicide prevention

Assistance is given to students and professionals who are involved in relevant research. PAPYRUS members are actively engaged in identifying predisposing factors in the light of their own experiences.

Being represented in policy-making decisions at all levels

In addition to working with Health Authorities, PAPYRUS has forged links with many MPs, has also responded to the Green Papers 'Our Healthier Nation', 'Better Health, Better Wales' and members have met with the All Party Group on Clinical Depression in the House of Commons.

Promoting the inclusion of good mental health policies in schools, colleges and universities

We have had articles published in both *The Times Educational Supplement* and *The Times Higher*, and have sent our views to the Personal, Social and Health Education Advisory Group set up by the Government.

Ensuring that adequate mental health services are available for young people

There should be an easily accessible route to such help on an informal, independent basis. We can provide information to schools and others on the various agencies and organisations that are available to help them.

Providing useful information for concerned parents/carers of suicidal young people

PAPYRUS can send a list of helpful organisations who can provide support, directly or through their literature.

Encouraging the provision of appropriate support

Where a suicide has already occurred, we can offer contact with organisations such as The Compassionate Friends and Survivors of Bereavement by Suicide (SOBS).

We encourage communication at all levels and welcome any enquiries.

What of the future?

PAPYRUS hopes to use its members' experiences and views to enlighten others in the recognition and management of potentially suicidal young people.

Some stark facts

In the UK, suicide is now the second most common cause of death (after road accidents) for young people between the ages of 15-24.

At the turn of the Millennium approximately 500 males and 100 females in the UK in this age group will kill themselves.

In Scotland young men are twice as likely to kill themselves as to die in road accidents.

In half of all suicides, the people who took their lives were not classified as being mentally ill.

For further information about PAPYRUS send SAE to:

Rossendale GH, Union Road, Rawtenstall, Rossendale, BB4 6NE. Tel: 01706 214449. E-mail: papyrus_uk@hotmail.com
When the office is closed details may be left on our secure answering service which is regularly checked.

© *PAPYRUS (Prevention of Suicides)*
January, 2000

Helping young people

Information from The Samaritans

The Samaritans' statistics

Contacts

In 1998, The Samaritans received 4,497,000 calls from people in despair. 36% of these calls were 'silent' calls where the caller did not make verbal contact.

Means of contact

By far the most common method of contact (96%) was by telephone. Additionally, callers made approximately 100,000 drop-in visits, 2,700 contacts by letter and approximately 15,000 contacts by e-mail.

Who contacts?

The Samaritans receive more calls from men than from women. 1,470,000 contacts came from men (50.9%), 1,346,000 from women (46.6%). Because of the confidential, anonymous nature of the service, sometimes it is not possible to identify the sex of the caller. This was the case in 2.5% of contacts.

Suicidal feelings

68% of the contacts reached a point where the volunteer was able to explore suicidal feelings of the caller. In 22% of these (433,000 calls) the caller expressed suicidal feelings at the time of the call. Of those who contacted by e-mail, 51% of contacts were from callers who were suicidal.

Volunteers

At the end of 1998, Samaritan volunteers number 19,600.

Hours of listening

Last year volunteers gave 3.1 million hours of listening to provide confidential emotional support to callers in crisis, an average of 180 hours or 22.5 working days per volunteer. If Samaritan volunteers were to be paid at the national minimum wage, the cost to the nation would be £11,134,000 per year.

Suicide statistics 1997

- 5,993* suicides in the UK, 433* suicides in the Republic of Ireland in 1997.
- One suicide every 82 minutes in UK and Ireland.
- 50% increase in Irish suicide and 18% increase in Scottish suicide since 1987.
- 75% of suicides are by males.
- 869* suicides by young people in UK and Ireland – more than 2 per day.
- Suicide accounts for 18% of all deaths of young people.
- Rising trend in attempted suicide – 70% increase since 1990.
- Suicide attempts by young men have risen by 172% since 1985.
- 26% of the population personally know someone who died by suicide.

*Data includes deaths by injury undetermined whether accidental or purposeful. Figures for England and Wales registered deaths, excluding ICD category E988.8. Data for Republic of Ireland refer to recorded suicides only (ICD E950-9).

Key facts: Young people and suicide

Suicide risk

- In 1997, 766 young people aged between 15 and 24 died by suicide in the UK. This is two young suicides every day. Over 80% are by young men.[1]
- Suicide is a major cause of death in young people. It accounts for over a fifth (21%) of all deaths of young people aged 20-24. In young men of this age group, suicide accounts for nearly a quarter (24%) of all deaths, in young women the figure is 14%.[2]
- The suicide rate amongst young men (aged between 15 and 24 years) has risen alarmingly over the 1980s and 1990s in the UK. Since 1993, there appears to have been a downturn in this trend, however rates are still higher than the overall population.

- Significant upward trend in young male suicides also occurring in the Republic of Ireland, which has seen an enormous 74% increase since 1985.[2]
- By contrast, the suicide rate for young women aged between 15 and 24 is 4 in every 100,000,[1] a quarter of the rate of their male peers.

Attempted suicide

- Attempted suicide is a major health problem amongst young people, their rates of attempting being much higher than the rest of the population. Young women and girls (aged between 15 and 19) make the highest number of suicide attempts each year.[3]
- There has recently been a particularly large increase in the rate of attempted suicide by young men and boys aged 15-24, whose rates have more than doubled since the mid 1980s.[3]
- In young women the trend is less marked but there has been a 42% increase in attempts by those of 15-24 years since 1992.[3]
- A conservative estimate is that there are 19,000 cases of attempted suicide by adolescents (of 10-19 years) each year in England and Wales, which is one attempt every 30 minutes.[4]
- At the time of the attempt, the most frequently-mentioned problems of young people were:
- relationship difficulties with a partner;
- relationship difficulties with a family member;
- employment/studies (far more commonly mentioned by males).[5]

Cultural differences

- Young women aged 15-24 who are of South Asian origin (i.e. Indian, Pakistani or Bangladeshi) are at much higher risk than other women living in the UK and Wales. [6,7]

- Young women born in the Indian sub-continent also show higher rates of attempted suicide[8] and culture conflict, family and marital problems are commonly cited problems.[6]

The role of alcohol and other drugs

- Approximately one in three adolescents who die by suicide is intoxicated at the time of death, and a further number are under the influence of drugs.[9]

Other factors

- Young suicide attempters report more 'significant others', i.e. people who have been important in their lives, who have attempted or died by suicide than other groups.[12]
- Adolescent attempters report less perceived support and understanding from their parents (specifically) than do depressed adolescents.[12] This does not appear to be the case for others in their social network such as friends, other family members and peers. The parental relationship appears to be an important factor.
- A study of young people between 11 and 16 who had self-poisoned found that poor family relationships, poverty and poor peer relationships were strongly associated with self-poisoning.[10]
- Research on prison suicides has shown that 30-50% are by young prisoners aged 16-25. Their motivations are often fear and helplessness and they are less likely to have a psychiatric history than older suiciders in prison.[11]
- An American study has shown a slightly but not significantly higher rate of homosexual experience amongst teenage suicides compared to teenage controls.[12]

References
1. Data from Office for National Statistics (England & Wales), Registrar General for Scotland, Registrar General for Northern Ireland, ICD codes E950-9 plus E980-9 (minus E988.8 for England and Wales).
2. Source: Central Statistics Office, Dublin. ICD codes E950-9 only.
3. Hawton, K, Fagg, J, Simkin, S, Bale, E and Bond, A. (unpublished), 'Attempted Suicide in Oxford 1995', enquiries to Professor Hawton, University Dept of Psychiatry, Warneford Hospital, Oxford OX3 7JX.
4. Hawton, K and Fagg, J. (1992), 'Deliberate Self-poisoning and Self-injury in Adolescents. A study of Characteristics and Trends in Oxford, 1976-89', British Journal of Psychiatry, 161, 816-23
5. Data obtained from Oxford Monitoring System, personal communication enquiries to Professor Hawton, University Dept of Psychiatry, Warneford Hospital, Oxford OX3 7JX.
6. Karmi, G, Abdulrahim, D, Pierpoint, T, McKeigue, P (unpublished), 'Suicide Among Ethnic Minorities and Refugees in the UK', The Health and Ethnicity Programme, NE & NW Thames RHA, London W2.
7. Soni Raleigh, V and Balarajan, R, (1992), 'Suicide and Self-burning among Indians and West Indians in England and Wales', British Journal of Psychiatry, 161, 365-8.
8. Merrill, J and Owens, J. (1986), 'Ethnic differences in self-poisoning: a comparison of Asian and white groups', British Journal of Psychiatry, 148, 708-12.
9. Brent, D, Perper, J, Goldsteing, CE, Kolko, D, Allan, MS, Allman, C, and Zelenak, J. (1986), 'Risk factors for adolescent suicide. A comparison of adolescent suicide victims with suicidal inpatients', Archives of General Psychiatry, 45, 581-8.
10. Kerfoot, M, Dyer, E, Harrington, V, Woodham, A and Harrington, R (1996), 'Correlates and Short-Term Course of Self-Poisoning in Adolescents', British Journal of Psychiatry, 168, 38-42.
11. Liebling, A and Krarup, H (1993), 'Suicide attempts and self-injury in male prisons', Home Office Library, London.
12. Shaffer, D, Fisher, P, Hicks, RH, Parides, M and Grould, M (1995), 'Sexual Orientation in Adolescents Who Commit Suicide', Suicide and Life-Threatening Behaviour, 25, Supplement, 64-71 Section eleven Page 4.

- The above informatioon is an extract from The Samaritans' Youth Pack. See page 41 for address details.

© The Samaritans

Suicide rates

European suicide rates per 100,000

Country	Year	Males	Female
Austria	1997	30.0	10.0
Belgium	1992	26.7	11.0
Denmark	1996	24.3	9.8
Finland	1996	38.7	10.7
France	1995	30.4	10.8
Germany	1997	22.1	8.1
Greece	1996	5.7	1.2
Ireland	1995	17.9	4.6
Italy	1993	12.7	4.0
Netherlands	1995	13.1	6.5
Norway	1995	19.1	6.2
Poland	1996	24.1	4.6
Portugal	1996	10.3	3.1
Spain	1995	12.5	3.7
Sweden	1996	20.0	8.5
Switzerland	1994	30.9	12.2
United Kingdom	1997	11.0	3.2

Source: World Health Organisation 2000, (www.who.int)

Suicide and young people

Information from ChildLine

Six weeks ago a friend of mine took an overdose. She was under a lot of pressure and couldn't tell anybody. She said she really wanted to die and wouldn't let me phone for an ambulance or call her parents . . . so I called ChildLine.

'I'd just like to say how brilliant they were. They talked to her and stayed on the phone while the ambulance was coming, and also helped me afterwards. I never believed that ChildLine could be so helpful but they saved my friend's life.'

Letter to magazine problem page

Feelings of despair, isolation and hopelessness can affect anyone of any age, at any time. When these feelings become too much to bear, it can seem to some young people that suicide is the only way to escape their problems.

Some facts and figures about suicide

(statistics provided by The Samaritans, December 1999)

- Suicide amongst young men aged 15-24 increased by 64% in the ten years up until 1994.
- Young women aged 15-19 years are at greatest risk of suicide attempts.
- 766 people aged between 15-24 killed themselves in the UK in 1997 (two every day).
- Suicide is now the second most common cause of death in the UK (after accidents) for young people aged 15-24.
- One person in a hundred who makes a serious suicide attempt will kill themselves within a year.
- 80% of suicides in the 15-24 age group are by young men.
- Self-harm among young men has almost doubled since the mid 1980s.
- There are 19,000 cases of attempted suicide every year by 10-19-year-olds in England and Wales.

What causes some young people to feel suicidal?

There is no simple explanation for suicidal behaviour. Calls to Child-Line show that abuse, constant rows with someone close, bullying, stress over exams, and worries about the future are just some of the things that, in some young people, can cause feelings of anxiety, low self-esteem, hopelessness and isolation. This can lead to thoughts of suicide. Groups particularly at risk of suicide include unemployed or homeless young people, young gay men and lesbians and young people who have problems with drugs.

Depression and despair can also be caused by specific events, such as the death of someone, parents splitting up, unwanted pregnancy, a relationship ending, or a violent incident such as rape. Sometimes young people, like adults, can feel deeply unhappy for no obvious reason at all, and believe that they will feel that way forever.

What do young people tell ChildLine about feeling suicidal?

Some young people who talk to ChildLine about feeling suicidal have actually made an attempt – such as an overdose – just before calling, and

---

Poster alert over suicide epidemic in young men

By Celia Hall, Medical Editor

The suicide rate in young men is one of the most important public health problems facing Britain, experts said yesterday.

Prof Sir Donald Acheson, former Government chief medical officer, said the suicides represented the 'tip of a huge iceberg of despair and misery in young people'. He was speaking at the start of a campaign aimed at helping men to talk about their problems. It will see 10,000 posters displayed.

Dr Ian Banks, chairman of the Men's Health Forum, said: 'The problem is really very serious. The trouble is that the statistics just do not show the scale of the human misery. For every child who commits suicide there will be a family that is destroyed and a school that is devastated. We have to act to stop this dreadful epidemic of human misery.'

Suicides in men aged 15 to 24, which had been static since the beginning of the century, rose by 80 per cent between 1982 and 1996. The latest available figures show that in 1997 suicides and deaths from self-inflicted and undetermined injury among 15 to 24-year-old boys and men were 549. That compared to 124 for young women.

GPs might be missing the warning signs, said Dr Simon Fradd, a Nottingham GP and chairman of the Doctor Patient Partnership – which is running the campaign with The Samaritans and the Men's Health Forum.

Studies show that many people who killed themselves had visited their doctors in the preceding weeks. Dr Fradd said: 'Often men will come to their GP and will not talk about the depression or suicidal tendencies.'

- The Samaritans are getting an increasing number of e-mails asking for help. In 1997, the charity had 7,500; last year there were 15,000. This year up to 25,000 are expected. They are answered within 24 hours.

© Telegraph Group Limited, London 1999

need immediate medical help. Others are feeling so unhappy about problems in their lives that they say or imply they are thinking of killing themselves. Some have felt depressed for a long time, while others are reacting to a recent event. Some have only just started thinking about suicide, but others have already made suicide attempts in the past.

Although, deep down, many of the young people who call ChildLine feeling suicidal may not really want to die, they tell us that at the time death feels like the only way of dealing with their problems.

They find it hard to look at other options, and often feel that all other solutions won't work. Their self-esteem may be so low that they believe they are a burden, and that their family, or the world, would be happier and better off without them. They may believe that people around them will be 'punished' by their death.

How do ChildLine counsellors help young people who feel suicidal?

Just picking up the phone and ringing ChildLine is an important step for a young person to take. Talking, being listened to and being taken seriously can make all the difference between a young person choosing to live or die. Callers often tell ChildLine how important it was for them to have someone who took the time to listen, to try to understand how they were feeling, and to be there for them at a time of crisis in their lives.

While taking seriously the young person's thoughts of suicide, ChildLine counsellors also help them to work out what has contributed to their depression, and look with them at ways of changing or coping with their situation. Callers are encouraged to talk about any feelings of pain, loss, anger and unhappiness, without being judged.

Counsellors help callers feel valued, and build up their confidence and sense of self-worth. Thoughts of suicide may take time to subside, or reoccur later, so callers are encouraged to call back, or get support from someone close.

Counsellors can also offer practical help, like giving information about help available in the young person's area, such as face-to-face counselling. If a caller's life is in immediate danger, for example from an overdose of tablets, counsellors will get help from the emergency services.

Some more facts about suicide

- People who make suicide attempts or threats are not just 'attention seeking', but are at risk of harming themselves.
- Anyone who talks about killing himself or herself, or tries to do it, is deeply unhappy, and needs help.
- Most suicidal people are undecided about living or dying, and try beforehand to let others know how they are feeling, or give clues and warnings.
- Talking about suicide with someone will not make them more likely to harm themselves.
- Every year around 2000 children and young people talk to ChildLine about feeling suicidal.

How ChildLine can help

ChildLine takes children and young people's problems seriously, giving them a chance to talk in confidence about their concerns, however large or small. ChildLine counsellors can also tell them where to go for more information including local sources of help and advice. This service is free and available 24 hours a day, 7 days a week on:
ChildLine: Freephone 0800 1111
or
Freepost 1111
London N1 OBR
or
ChildLine Minicom: 0800 400 222
Mon-Fri 9.30am-9.30pm
Sat-Sun 9.30am-8.00pm

Other sources of help

Samaritans:
numbers of local branches are in the phone-book,
or
0345 909090, a national number with calls charged at local rates
or
e-mail: jo@samaritans.org.uk

Young Minds
Information on mental health issues and young people is available from Young Minds, 102-108 Clerkenwell Road, London EC1M 5SA.

© *ChildLine*
February, 2000

Signs of suicide risk

Has the person experienced any of the following:
- recent loss (a loved one, pet, job); the recent break-up of a close relationship; a major disappointment (failed exams, missed job promotion); a change in circumstances (retirement, redundancy, children leaving home); physical/mental illness?

Has s/he:
- made a previous suicide attempt; a history of suicide in the family; begun tidying up their affairs (making a will, taking out insurance)?

Visual clues:
Is s/he:
- Withdrawn; low-spirited? finding it difficult to relate to others; taking less care of themselves; different in some way, for example, unusually cheerful; tearful or trying hard not to cry; more irritable; finding it hard to concentrate; less energetic and seems particularly tired; eating less (or more) than usual?

Things to listen for:
Does s/he talk about:
- Feeling suicidal (it's a myth that people who talk about it don't do it); seeing no hope in the future, no point in life; feeling worthless, a failure; feeling very isolated and alone; sleeping badly, especially waking early; losing their appetite or eating more than usual?

© *The Samaritans*

Men behaving sadly

Help is at hand. Information from the Royal College of Psychiatrists

Suicide

Men are around 3 times more likely to kill themselves than women. Suicide is commonest amongst men who are separated, widowed or divorced and is more likely if someone is a heavy drinker. Over the last few years men have become more likely to kill themselves, particularly those aged between 16 and 24 years and those between 39 and 54 years. We don't yet know why this should be so, but it is very worrying.

We do know that 2 out of 3 people who kill themselves have seen their GP in the previous 4 weeks and nearly 1 in every 2 will have done so in the week before they kill themselves. We also know that about 2 out of 3 people who kill themselves will have talked about it to friends or family.

Asking if someone is feeling this way will not put the idea into his head or make it more likely that he will kill himself. So, although some men may not be very good at talking about how they are feeling, it is important to ask if you have any suspicion – and to take such ideas seriously. For a man who feels suicidal, there is nothing more demoralising than to feel that others do not take him seriously. He will often have taken some time to pluck up the courage to tell anybody about it. If you do find yourself feeling so bad that you have thought about suicide, it can be a great relief to tell someone.

Violence

Some studies have shown that men who commit violent crimes are more likely to get depressed than men who don't. However, we don't know if the depression makes their violence more likely, or if it's just the way they lead their lives.

Helping men

Many men find it difficult to ask for help when they are depressed – it

can feel unmanly and weak. It may be easier for men to ask for help if those who give that help take into account men's special needs.

Men who are depressed are more likely to talk about the physical symptoms of their depression rather than the emotional and psychological ones. This may be one reason why doctors sometimes don't diagnose it. If you are feeling wretched, don't hold back – tell your GP.

It can help to be reminded that depression is a result of chemical changes in the brain. It is nothing to do with being weak or unmanly, and it can easily be helped. Anti-depressant tablets are often an important part of getting better – and it's important to remember that this sort of medication is not addictive.

If a depressed man is married, or in a steady relationship, his partner should be involved so that she can understand what is happening. This will make it less likely for the depression to cause permanent problems in their relationship.

Some men don't feel comfortable talking about themselves and so may be reluctant to consider psychotherapy. However, it is a very powerful way of relieving depression and works well for many men.

Helping yourself

Don't bottle things up – If you've had a major upset in your life, try to tell someone how you feel about it.

Keep active

Get out of doors and get some exercise, even if it's only a walk. This will help to keep you physically fit and you will sleep better. It can also help you not to dwell unhelpfully on painful thoughts and feelings.

Eat properly

You may not feel very hungry, but you should eat a balanced diet, with lots of fruit and vegetables. It's easy to lose weight and run low on vitamins when you are depressed.

Avoid alcohol and drugs

Alcohol may make you feel better for a couple of hours, but it will make you more depressed in the long run. The same goes for street drugs, particularly amphetamines and ecstasy.

Don't get upset if you can't sleep
Do something restful that you enjoy, like listening to the radio or watching television.

Use relaxation techniques
If you feel tense all the time there are many ways of helping yourself to relax. These include exercises, audio-tapes, yoga, massage, aromatherapy etc.

Do something you enjoy
Set some time aside regularly each week to do something you really enjoy – exercise, reading, a hobby.

Check out your lifestyle
A lot of people who have depression are perfectionists and tend to drive themselves too hard. You may need to set yourself more realistic targets and reduce your workload.

Take a break
This may be easier said than done, but it can be really helpful to get away and out of your normal routine for a few days. Even a few hours can be helpful.

Read about depression
There are now many books about depression. They can help you to cope, but can also help friends and relatives to understand what you are going through.

Remember, in the long run, this might be helpful. It's unpleasant to have it, but depression can be a useful experience, and some people emerge stronger and coping better than before. You may see situations and relationships more clearly and may now have the strength and wisdom to make important decisions and changes that you were avoiding before.

Finding more help
The best place to start is your general practitioner. He or she will be able to assess you and to discuss the options for treatment with you. It is true that many men are concerned that the information held by their family doctors may need to be given in medical reports, and so may damage their chances in work. In spite of this, your GP is the best person to approach. Depression may be due to physical illness, so it is important that you have a proper physical check-up. If you are already receiving treatment for some physical disorder, your GP will need to know because of the possible interactions between drugs. Any worries about confidentiality should be discussed with your GP.

If you really feel that you can't talk about it with anyone you know, The Samaritans offer a 24-hour telephone service which can give you the opportunity to discuss things anonymously.

Depression can be as much of an illness as pneumonia or breaking your leg. We really shouldn't feel embarrassed or ashamed about it. The most important thing to remember is to ask for the help you need, when you need it. If you need more information, or to talk to somebody confidentially, the following list of publications may be helpful.

Remember – depression is easily treatable and you are entitled to the help you need.

• This article is from one of a series of leaflets for the general public entitled *Help is at Hand*. The other leaflets are entitled: *Alcohol and Depression, Bereavement, Depression, Depression in the Elderly, Depression in the Workplace, Depression in People with Learning Disability, Manic Depression, Memory and Dementia, Postnatal Depression, Sleeping Well, Social Phobias and Schizophrenia*. All the leaflets are available to download from the Royal College of Psychiatrists web site: www.rcpsych.ac.uk

Samaritans launch online schools pack

The Samaritans have launched an online youth pack to help schools tackle subjects such as depression and self-harm with their pupils. The charity says it is a direct response to rising suicide levels in people aged under 25.

Figures show that two young people kill themselves every day, and 19,000 cases of attempted suicide among adolescents are reported every year.

The pack, which is available on the charity's website and is aimed at secondary school pupils, has been designed to help teachers address problems pupils might be experiencing.

Classroom activities, such as role plays and workshops, have been designed to tie in with personal, social and health education lessons.

School visits
Chapters of the pack are dedicated to a variety of subjects, including fear, isolation, depression, self-harm and suicide.

Volunteers from The Samaritans can also visit schools to help teachers hold discussions and workshops.

The charity's youth co-ordinator Alison Weisselberg said: 'Pupils every day are struggling to cope with feelings of despair and anxiety resulting from bullying, exam stress, worries about sexual orientation and family problems.

'Having the youth pack online enables teachers to gain instant support and guidance in helping young people discuss these issues sensitively within the classroom.'

• The Samaritans' *Youth Pack* can be accessed at www.samaritans.org.uk/ Their postal address is listed on page 41.

Doctors declare war on male suicides

GPs need to get better at spotting the warning signs that a young man may be at risk of committing suicide, say doctors

Suicide is the second biggest cause of death among young men aged 15 to 24.

The Doctor Patient Partnership (DPP), the British Medical Association (BMA) and The Samaritans launched a major campaign on Tuesday to target young male suicides.

Posters will be placed in pubs, job centres and benefit centres to draw attention to the problem and where help is available.

Despite a slight fall over the past two years, the number of young men who commit suicide rose by 80% between 1980 and 1992. In 1995, the suicide rate among young men was 150 per million.

Although young women are more likely to attempt suicide, men tend to be more successful at it because they resort to more violent means to end their lives.

Every day two young adults in the UK take their lives and doctors and suicide campaigners have banded together to find ways to tackle the problem.

Many suicidal young men visit their GP within four weeks of taking their own lives, but doctors often fail to pick up the warning signs.

Dr Sunil Angris of the BMA's GP Committee says part of the problem is that young men are not as open about their feelings and problems as young women.

'Males tend not to open up while females are more likely to unload their stress,' he said.

Early warning signs

A DPP poll shows that GPs are usually the first professional port of call for suicidal young men.

Campaigners believe that a more informal approach by doctors to young men could make them feel more at ease and help them share their problems.

The DPP poll also shows that men would prefer to talk face to face with their families and partners about problems than discuss their worries over a helpline.

Seventy-one per cent said they would prefer face-to-face discussions about problems, compared with 8% who would choose a helpline and 1% who would consult the internet.

The Samaritans says they have walk-in centres where people can talk to trained counsellors face to face, although people tend to associate the organisation only with its helpline.

Responsibilities

Simon Armson, chief executive of The Samaritans, said: 'We all have a responsibility to acknowledge that young men can suffer despairing and

suicidal feelings, although they might try to hide them.

'We must give men the time and space they need to talk openly about those feelings.'

DPP chair-man Dr Simon Fradd said: 'Young men are often reluctant to talk about their problems and are sometimes too ashamed to seek help from their GP.

'What we are trying to say to these young people is that they should talk to their GP about their feelings and that the GP should reassure them that any conversation is strictly confidential.'

Men's Health Forum, an organisation representing approximately 100 groups with an interest in the subject, is to undertake research into why so many young men kill themselves, and into how access to health care professionals can be improved.

Chairman Dr Ian Banks said many men were reluctant to talk about their feelings because of the 'stiff upper lip' culture.

'It is not only tragic, it is a national disgrace for so many potential years of life to be lost by these young men taking their lives in such numbers.

'GPs as well as the government have to play their part in addressing this epidemic of human misery.'

Professor Sir Donald Acheson, former Chief Medical Officer and author of a major report into health inequalities last year, said: 'Suicide in men and in particular unskilled young men is one of the most important public health problems of our times.

'It is also the tip of a huge iceberg of despair and misery.'

Drive to reduce suicides

Information from BBC News Online

The number of people committing suicide should be reduced by 20% in the next 10 years – saving up to 4,000 lives in total, according to the government's White Paper on public health.

The figure is up by 3% from that contained in the Green Paper on public health.

The government estimates more than one person dies every two hours from suicide, although England's suicide rate is amongst the lowest in the European Union.

Some professions, such as farmers and doctors, are more at risk because of easier access to the means for committing suicide.

Mental illness is thought to cost the country £32.1m.

Mental health charities welcome the White Paper's focus on identifying and dealing with the possible factors behind mental illness, such as social exclusion and unemployment. But they say the Department of Health would do better to invest more money in support services for those who are ill than setting suicide targets.

The government recommends a range of measures to improve mental health, including setting up a Task Force, headed by a well-known figure, to champion mental health, strengthening support systems and raising awareness of mental health, including in schools.

Also mentioned in the White Paper are:

- Plans to reduce access to methods of suicide, such as controlling pack sizes for paracetamol
- Developing NHS Direct and links to specialist mental health helplines
- Improving follow-up for people who have attempted suicide
- Setting good practice guidelines
- Supporting people at high risk of suicide
- Ensuring mental health is a key outcome of other social inclusion programmes
- Auditing suicides to learn prevention lessons.

It says specific standards for improving mental health will be set out in new national service frameworks.

One in four

An estimated one in four of the population is affected by mental illness.

The Samaritans, which operates a helpline for people who are feeling depressed and suicidal, says it is receiving an increasing number of calls from people with major mental health problems.

It 'welcomes and considers essential the inclusion of a specific suicide reduction target' in the White Paper.

But it would like to see different targets for different groups.

'This would reflect the considerable variations between suicide rates that exist for different population groups,' it said.

One of the highest risk groups for suicide is currently young men.

Suicide is currently the second biggest cause of death for men aged 15 to 24.

Although women are more likely to attempt suicide, young men are more likely to be successful.

One target

The Samaritans also expressed concerns about having just one national target for mental health.

Shadow health secretary Dr Liam Fox said it was debatable whether suicide was the best way to measure mental health.

But the King's Fund health charity says the government's policy

> *Suicide is currently the second biggest cause of death for men aged 15 to 24*

has been to reduce the previous administration's concentration on national targets and to focus instead on setting local priorities.

A spokesman said this would help to involve people more in public health improvements and would therefore be more likely to achieve success.

'It is very hard to have headline indicators for mental health,' he said. 'A lot depends on local action.'

He added that mental health problems could be very different from one community to another.

Judi Clements of Mind welcomed the White Paper's focus on poverty and deprivation.

'Tackling the root causes of mental health problems with preventative measures is far more effective in the long term than traditional symptom-based treatments.'

She said the mental health strategy needed to be integrated with other social exclusion policies and to be sufficiently monitored.

Mind also wants to see the health skills programme announced in the White Paper include emotional and mental well-being as well as physical health.

Marjorie Wallace of mental health charity SANE said the focus on public awareness of mental health was good, but there was no point in creating more awareness if crisis services were not available.

'It would be better if they could set more realistic aims about improving mental health services for all those who need them,' she said.

But she added that this would involve more resources being poured into increasing the number of beds for mentally ill people, the number of staff working in the field and the availability of new, more effective drugs.

© Courtesy of BBC News Online (http://news.bbc.co.uk) January, 2000

Saving lives: mental health

Saving Lives: Our Healthier Nation is an action plan by the Government to tackle poor health

Target: to reduce the death rate from suicide and undetermined injury by at least a fifth by 2010 – saving up to 4,000 lives in total.

Mental health is as important to an individual as good physical health. Mental health influences how we feel, perceive, think, communicate and understand. Without good mental health, people can be unable to fulfil their full potential or play an active part in everyday life.

Mental health problems are a major cause of ill-health, disability and mortality. They include:

- depression and anxiety – extremely common in both urban and rural areas, often disabling and may last a long time if untreated
- schizophrenia – relatively rare but often extremely severe, disabling and long-term
- bipolar affective disorder (formerly known as manic depression) – relatively rare, episodic in nature and often very severe
- dementia – common in older people, involving progressive deterioration of intellectual and social functioning, with no recovery
- anti-social personality disorder – which contributes to crime and aggression.

People with mental illness may have difficulties in sustaining supportive relationships with friends, family and colleagues; with parenting; with work and other daily activities. They may have higher rates of substance misuse. These social consequences of mental illness increase the stigma and social exclusion suffered by people with mental illness and that, in turn, makes the original condition worse.

More people who are worse off financially and socially, particularly in inner cities, have mental illness; more contemplate suicide and more actually commit suicide than people who are better off. For example:

- unemployed people are twice as likely to suffer from depression as people in work
- children in the poorest households are three times more likely to have mental ill-health than children in the best-off households
- people sleeping rough or using night shelters are four times more likely to have a mental disorder than the general population
- people in prisons are at least fifteen times more likely to have a psychotic disorder than the general population
- refugees have higher rates of mental disorder than the general population.

In England, on average, more than one person dies every two hours as a result of suicide. Suicidal thoughts are quite common but are seldom acted on. But if a quick and lethal method of suicide is readily at hand someone might act impulsively without allowing time for second thoughts or rescue. So there are more suicides among those who have easy access to the means of killing themselves such as guns, certain medicines or chemicals. That is one of the reasons why suicide figures are high for some professional groups such as doctors, nurses, farmers, vets and pharmacists.

Many people who are mentally ill die prematurely from physical illness, especially respiratory illness, cancer or coronary heart disease. People with eating disorders and those involved in substance misuse are at highest risk, although the risks are almost as great for those with schizophrenia or major depression.

People with mental illness may suffer considerable fear, mental pain and distress, sometimes for many years, taking a considerable toll on themselves and their families. They may be socially excluded because of their mental illness. Besides the immense cost in personal suffering which mental illness carries, it has a high economic cost as well. A recent study estimated that the cost in England amounted to £32.1 billion.

How do we compare?
Suicide rates within the UK are reasonably similar in England, Wales and Northern Ireland but are higher in Scotland. Suicide rates in England are among the lowest in the European Union.

Causes
Detailed research on the causes of mental illness has shown that the major risk factors for mental illness include:

- poverty, poor education, unemployment
- social isolation stemming from discrimination against people with all types of physical disabilities
- major life events such as bereavement, redundancy, financial problems, being the victim of crime
- genetic predisposition
- drug and alcohol misuse
- developmental factors such as foetal damage and injury at birth
- poor parenting.

Action: promoting good mental health and reducing risk
Promoting good mental health is relevant to everyone. We can all enhance our mental well-being through some simple steps which make it easier for us to cope with the problems and pressures of daily life. These can be as straightforward as keeping in touch with our family and friends, and keeping involved with our local community. Making time for relaxation and for physical activity can reduce stress, while asking for help and talking problems over can also prevent mental health problems from building up.

We are promoting these simple steps through national public

education campaigns, for use in a wide range of settings. Schools, workplaces, neighbourhoods and prisons should all play their part in improving mental health as well as improving health generally.

In addition it is possible to reduce the risk of various mental illnesses, such as depression, by strengthening support systems; dementia by stopping smoking, adopting a healthy diet and being physically active; relapse in schizophrenia by specific family interventions; and suicide through a range of specific measures.

For example unemployed people are less likely to suffer depression and to have better success finding work if they are given social support and help in developing job-seeking skills; people caring for relatives with dementia are less likely to suffer from depression if they are given practical information about the disease. Similarly people caring for relatives with schizophrenia benefit from practical information and social support; support groups supplying a combination of practical help, social networking and advice on parenting have also been proven to have a dramatic impact on the mental health of young isolated mothers and on the cognitive and emotional development of their pre-school children. Rapid treatment for depressed mothers can prevent harm to the children who may otherwise experience cognitive and emotional damage. Self-help support groups have proved beneficial for widows where they can offer each other one-to-one support alongside other practical help and small group meetings. Children at school with unrecognised learning difficulties including dyslexia will benefit from appropriate school programmes for assessment and help.

Children whose parents are divorcing can benefit from school-based help and parents can be taught parenting skills.

CALM – The Campaign Against Living Miserably
CALM is a pilot helpline in Manchester, funded by the Department of Health, offering a safety net for young men with mental ill-health. It aims to tackle the stigma attached to depression and mental illness and encourage take-up of the services available. It is staffed by trained counsellors who offer advice, guidance and information. We are looking to build on the success of CALM by making the helpline available in other areas, in partnership with local agencies and authorities.

We can reduce suicide through the following steps:

- reduce access to methods of suicide, such as controlling the pack sizes for paracetamol available off the shelf
- develop NHS Direct, networked to specialist mental health helplines, as a source of advice for those in mental distress
- good assessment and follow-up of people who attempt to kill themselves
- use good practice guidelines on looking after suicidal people in primary and specialist care
- continue professional training about prompt detection, assessment, diagnosis and treatment of depression and assessment of suicidal risk
- support people who are at high risk of suicide, particularly people with severe mental illness and those in high-risk occupations
- develop mental health promotion strategies in schools, workplaces and prisons which enhance social support and coping strategies and which tackle bullying
- work with the media to ensure responsible reporting of suicides which neither glamorises the event nor publishes the method used
- audit suicides in order to learn the lessons for prevention.

We support the National Confidential Inquiry into Suicide and Homicide which audits suicides across the country.

Action: early recognition
There are far more people with a mental health problem than the specialist services see. Some of them will seek help from families and friends. Many will be seen by their family doctor but mental health problems can be difficult to diagnose, especially when the patient has physical symptoms or learning difficulties or if there is a language or other cultural barrier. On average, family doctors identify only about half of the people who come to them with depression and anxiety, and not

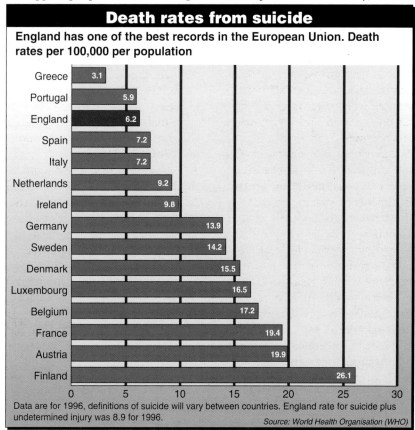

Death rates from suicide

England has one of the best records in the European Union. Death rates per 100,000 per population

Greece	3.1
Portugal	5.9
England	6.2
Spain	7.2
Italy	7.2
Netherlands	9.2
Ireland	9.8
Germany	13.9
Sweden	14.2
Denmark	15.5
Luxembourg	16.5
Belgium	17.2
France	19.4
Austria	19.9
Finland	26.1

Data are for 1996, definitions of suicide will vary between countries. England rate for suicide plus undetermined injury was 8.9 for 1996.

Source: World Health Organisation (WHO)

all of those receive the right treatment. Some patients first come into contact with the police or social services rather than a hospital or a family doctor. For all these reasons it is important that people in the relevant agencies, especially those in the health service, have the skills to recognise the symptoms of mental illness.

Mental health is the subject of one of the first two new National Service Frameworks. The Framework will set national standards and define service models for mental health promotion, suicide prevention, assessment, diagnosis, treatment, rehabilitation and care. We shall use the Framework to ensure that these professional staff have the skills to detect early signs of mental illness and to assess suicidal risk; and we are ensuring that mental health teams have the necessary skills for relapse prevention, including for those with concomitant substance misuse.

Action: effective treatment

We can achieve a great deal by promoting good mental health, preventing illness and by prompt and effective treatment in primary care. Our Healthy Citizens initiative will help individuals to take control of their own mental health, through making use of NHS Direct, through developing their health skills and through our Expert Patients programme. But there will always be a need for effective specialist mental health services. Access to specialist treatment and care varies across the country as well as by age, ethnic group, gender, and social class. We therefore need to ensure that people suffering from mental ill-health have access to consistently high-quality treatment and care services suited to their needs. To achieve this, in December 1998 we published *Modernising Mental Health Services – safe, sound and supportive*, setting out in detail our strategy for ensuring effective mental health services. That strategy made mental health a national priority across both health and social care services.

Secondly we have launched a fundamental review of the law on mental health to ensure that it is brought up to date to reflect modern practice. It will report in the summer.

Thirdly the National Service Framework for Mental Health, to be implemented from April 2000, will ensure the development of consistent high-quality services which cross professional and agency boundaries, and which are equally accessible to all.

Integrated action

If we are to promote mental health and reduce not only mental illness but also its adverse impact on individuals and families we need to:

- ensure that mental health is regarded as a key outcome of each strand of the Government's agenda to promote social inclusion – from Sure Start to Better Government for Older People; from the Rough Sleepers Initiative to the Welfare to Work programme, and across the range of local initiatives
- put in place the range of action to reduce suicide – within the NHS and partner agencies, the media and those who can help to reduce access to the methods of suicide
- strengthen the capacity of primary care services to identify, assess and treat those with mental health problems
- ensure effective care for those with severe mental illness; and better support for those who care for them.

The National Service Framework for Mental Health will cover these areas – setting out standards and service models with a clear drive towards implementation and delivery. It will be a key element in meeting our target for reducing suicides. It will address the whole range of mental health service provision, from primary care, where the majority of mental health problems can be managed, through to specialist mental health services. This will help to ensure that people with mental health problems receive the service they need, regardless of who they are or where they live.

We shall bring together the implementation of this contract for mental health with the delivery of the National Service Framework for Mental Health by setting up a high-level Task Force, accountable to the Chief Medical Officer. The Task Force will ensure that the essential ground work is laid to set us on course for achieving our target for saving lives which would otherwise be lost to suicide. We will identify someone of national prominence to act as its champion, whose function will be to build and maintain momentum for action, to communicate the purpose of the contract and to encourage individuals to commit themselves to it.

We will use the Public Health Development Fund to support the achievement of our target for mental health.

- The above is an extract from *Saving Lives: Our Healthier Nation*, the Government's White Paper.

Prevention of suicidal behaviours

A task for all. Information from the World Health Organisation

Background

The problem

- In the year 2000, approximately one million people will die from suicide: a 'global' mortality rate of 16 per 100,000, or one death every 40 seconds.
- In the last 45 years suicide rates have increased by 60% worldwide. Suicide is now among the three leading causes of death among those aged 15-44 years (both sexes); these figures do not include suicide attempts, up to 20 times more frequent than completed suicide.
- Suicide worldwide is estimated to represent 1.8% of the total global burden of disease in 1998, and 2.4% in countries with market and former socialist economies in 2020.
- Although traditionally suicide rates have been highest among the male elderly, rates among young people have been increasing to such an extent that they are now the group at highest risk in a third of countries, in both developed and developing countries.
- Mental disorders (particularly depression and substance abuse) are associated with more than 90% of all cases of suicide; however, suicide results from many complex socio-cultural factors and is more likely to occur particularly during periods of socio-economic, family and individual crisis situations (e.g. loss of a loved one, employment, honour).

Effective interventions

- Strategies involving restriction of access to common methods of suicide have proved to be effective in reducing suicide rates; however, there is a need to adopt multi-sectoral approaches involving other levels of intervention and activities, such as crisis centres.
- There is compelling evidence indicating that adequate prevention and treatment of depression, alcohol and substance abuse can reduce suicide rates.
- School-based interventions involving crisis management, self-esteem enhancement and the development of coping skills and healthy decision making have been demonstrated to reduce the risk of suicide among the youth.

Challenges and obstacles

- Worldwide, the prevention of suicide has not been adequately

addressed basically due to a lack of awareness of suicide as a major problem and the taboo in many societies to discuss it openly. In fact, only a few countries have included prevention of suicide among their priorities.
- Reliability of suicide certification and reporting is an issue in great need of improvement.
- It is clear that suicide prevention requires intervention also from outside the health sector and calls for an innovative, comprehensive multi-sectoral approach, including both health and non-health sectors, e.g. education, labour, police, justice, religion, law, politics, the media.

Objectives

The overall objective of this project is to reduce mortality and morbidity due to suicidal behaviours, breaking the taboo surrounding suicide and bringing together national authorities and the public in an integrated manner to overcome the challenges. Specific objectives are:

1. To bring about a lasting reduction in the number of suicides and suicide attempts, with emphasis on developing countries and countries in social and economic transition.
2. To identify, assess and eliminate at early stages, as far as possible, factors that may result in young people taking their own lives.
3. To raise the general awareness about suicide and provide psycho-social support to people with suicidal thoughts or experiences of attempted suicide, and to their relatives and close friends, as well as to those of people who committed suicide.

© World Health Organisation 2000
(www.who.int)

Losing someone we love

Information from CRUSE

We are each individuals and when we lose someone we love, we lose not only a person who was special and unique but a relationship that was unique too. And yet when we grieve, most of us follow a similar journey from the first shock and disbelief through the waves of intense sadness and pain, the looking back over the past, the regrets, the longings, the loneliness, perhaps anger and depression too, through to the time when it becomes possible to begin to rebuild our lives again.

There is no 'right' way to grieve and we each react in our own way. Some people are able to carry on almost normally, while others may feel for a time as if they are falling apart.

Healing comes slowly, but it does come. Nothing can replace the person who has died and yet gradually we do find new sources of strength within ourselves that help us to survive. Some people find it easier to show their feelings than others, but most find at some stage that it helps to talk.

Life turned upside down

When a death occurs many people find their whole way of life is changed; their day-to-day routine as well as their hopes and plans for the future may be completely overturned. Although the deep hurt that we feel may make us want to crawl away like a wounded animal to some dark corner and stay there, we usually have to face up to all sorts of practical problems. Forms have to be filled in and there may be difficulties with money, accommodation, keeping a job going, disposing of a home and its possessions or worrying about who will look after children or elderly relatives. All these pressures come at a time when, because of our grief, we feel less able to cope with them, and we may need to get practical advice from someone we trust, who can help us sort out which problems have to

be dealt with urgently and which ones can be left until later when we are better able to take a decision.

Although most people's thoughts will be turned inwards to their hurt and sadness at this time, keeping going with a job or regular routine can help to hold together the framework of our life. The people at work, or simply getting on with what has to be done, whether inside or outside the home, can help us through even though we may have little energy and find little meaning in what we are doing.

I can't believe it

We feel shock when someone dies and the first reaction is often that it cannot be true.

The shock can affect us physically and may make us feel numb, stunned and unreal. It is hard to believe that the person we love will no longer come walking in through the door.

When the death has been sudden or unexpected it is especially hard to accept that it has happened, but it can also be difficult when there has been a long illness beforehand.

Because we so much wish it had

not happened, the truth takes time to sink in. The reality of the funeral and the presence there of family and friends can help us to begin to accept the fact that the person we love has died.

Why did it have to happen?

Death can seem cruel and unfair, and especially so when we feel someone has died before their time.

Although we know that as human beings we all have to die and are no more protected from accident or tragedy than other people, the death of someone close to us shakes our sense of security and challenges our beliefs. Often we cannot help asking why it had to happen as it did.

There is no simple universal answer to this question, and part of the pain of grief lies in the struggle to find an answer or explanation that will help to make sense of a death that seems wasteful or senseless.

• The above information is an extract from *After the Death of Someone Very Close*, a booklet produced by CRUSE. See page 41 for address details.
© CRUSE

Supporting a child who is bereaved through suicide

Information from Winston's Wish

If death is still a difficult issue for people to discuss, then the death of a family member by suicide is perhaps one of the greatest challenges to society. There are still many taboos that exist when someone chooses to end their own life. People generally feel very uneasy when the subject of suicide is raised – feelings of horror and embarrassment are common.

People often use a variety of words to describe suicide including committing suicide, killing themselves and ending/taking their own life. Different families will feel comfortable with different words.

Your feelings

When a person has died by suicide the family is faced with many outsiders (e.g. the police, coroner, media etc.). The story of what happened and the family's grief can become very public. For these and other reasons it is generally best to be honest and open when talking about the death.

Even if someone has said that they intend to kill themselves, the death may come as a shock and it can take a long time before family members begin to believe it is true.

Where families have lived through 'threats' and previous attempts, relationships may have become strained and this, together with the contents of suicide notes, can make adjustment more complicated. It is not uncommon to see individual family members desperately trying to understand 'why' the person has killed themselves. In trying to understand 'why' they may seek to blame others in the family. This can make the situation more complicated, but is often very normal.

When a close family member has died by suicide, close relatives may have a very vivid picture of the way in which the person died – whether they discovered the body or not. It is not uncommon for this image to stay with the family for a long time. Different people may hold on to different pictures.

A sudden, unexpected death can have an impact on many people beyond the immediate circle of close family and friends (e.g. work colleagues, neighbours). By its nature suicide is often untimely, unexpected and often violent. Individual reactions vary – people may feel shock, disbelief, guilt, sadness and bewilderment. Anger and blame can occur, often resulting in painful family rifts. For example, an elderly mother may blame a recent divorce instigated by her daughter-in-law for her son's death.

If you are helping a child bereaved through suicide, you will also probably be experiencing your own reactions. Take time to consider your feelings and to talk to a trusted person about your own questions. By thinking through issues for yourself, this might help you to support others.

The future

Because suicide raises so many difficult questions and feelings, grieving can be very complicated. Children and grown-ups can be left wondering if there is something wrong with them for such a thing to have happened. Confidence can be overshadowed by a sense of failure and this can make optimism for the future difficult. For children, a belief in the future is very important. Small events to look forward to can provide goals. Praise and encouragement for the child in gaining new skills and achievements builds the child's positive identity.

A secure, consistent home life, with support from kind friends, will all help towards recovery. Don't be afraid to ask for help. It is often particularly helpful for children and parents to meet with others who share the same experience.

• The above information is an extract from *Supporting a child who is bereaved through suicide*, a leaflet produced by Winston's Wish. See page 41 for address details.

© *Winston's Wish*

ADDITIONAL RESOURCES

You might like to contact the following organisations for further information. Due to the increasing cost of postage, many organisations cannot respond to enquiries unless they receive a stamped, addressed envelope.

Befrienders International
26-27 Market Place
Kingston Upon Thames
Surrey, KT1 1JH
Tel: 020 8541 4949
Fax: 020 8549 1544
E-mail: admin@befrienders.org
Web site: www.befrienders.org
To build effective suicide prevention services world-wide resolved by volunteers.

ChildLine
2nd Floor Royal Mail Building
50 Studd Street
London, N1 0QW
Tel: 020 7239 1000
Fax: 020 7239 1001
E-mail: reception@childline.org.uk
Web site: www.childline.org.uk
ChildLine is a free, national help line for children and young people in trouble or danger. Provides confidential phone counselling service for any child with any problem 24 hours a day. Freephone 0800 1111. Produces publications.

Cruse Bereavement Care
Cruse House
126 Sheen Road
Richmond-upon-Thames, TW9 1UR
Tel: 020 8940 4818
Fax: 020 8940 7638
E-mail:
info@crusebereavementcare.org.uk
Offers counselling for all forms of bereavement.

Kidscape Campaign for Children's Safety
2 Grosvenor Gardens
London, SW1W 9TR
Tel: 020 7730 3300
Fax: 020 7730 7081
E-mail: info@kidscape.org.uk
Web site: www.kidscape.org.uk
Works to prevent the abuse of children through education involving parents and teachers. Produces a wide range of books and leaflets on child-related issues including bullying and child abuse. Ask for their publications list.

Mental Health Foundation
20-21 Cornwall Terrace
London, NW1 4QL
Tel: 020 7535 7400
Fax: 020 7535 7474
E-mail: mhf@mentalhealth.org.uk
Web site: www.mentalhealth.org.uk
Works to prevent mental disorder wherever possible by funding and supporting research and educating people about the causes and effects of stress.

MIND
Granta House
15-19 Broadway
Stratford
London, E15 4BQ
Tel: 020 8519 2122
Fax: 020 8522 1725
E-mail: contact@mind.org.uk
Web site: www.mind.org.uk
MIND is the leading mental health charity in England and Wales They produce a wide range of advice leaflets (£1.00 plus A5 sae), reports and books including *How to . . . help someone who is suicidal* from the series *How to . . .* Ask for their publications list.

Royal College of Psychiatrists
17 Belgrave Square
London, SW1X 8PG
Tel: 020 7235 2351
Fax: 020 7235 1935
E-mail: rcpsych@rcpsych.ac.uk
Web site: www.rcpsych.ac.uk
Produces an excellent series of free leaflets on various aspects of mental health. Supplied free of charge but a stamped, addressed envelope is required.

The Samaritans
10 The Grove
Slough, SL1 1QP
Tel: 01753 532713
Fax: 01753 819004
E-mail: admin@samaritans.org.uk
Web site: www.samaritans.org.uk
Deals with suicide-related issues. Help line open 24 hours 0345 909090

Trust for the Study of Adolescence (TSA)
23 New Road
Brighton, BN1 1WZ
Tel: 01273 693 311
Fax: 01273 679 907
E-mail: info@tsa.uk.com
Web site: www.tsa.uk.com
TSA is an organisation which promotes the study of adolescence. Their aim is to work towards a wider understanding of this stage of human development. Produces various publications.

Winston's Wish
Gloucester Royal Hospital
Great Western Road
Gloucester, GL1 3NN
Tel: 01452 394377
Fax: 01452 395656
E-mail: info@winstonswish.org.uk
Web site:
www.winstonswish.org.uk
A grief support programme for bereaved children and their families.

World Health Organisation (WHO)
20 Avenue Appia
1211-GENEVA 27
Switzerland
Tel: 00 41 22 791 2111
Fax: 00 41 22 791 3111
E-mail: registry@who.ch
Web site: www.who.ch
WHO works to make a difference in the lives of the world's people by enhancing both life expectancy and health expectancy.

Young Minds
102-108 Clerkenwell Road
London, EC1M 5SA
Tel: 020 7336 8445
Fax: 020 7336 8446
E-mail: enquiries@youngminds.org.uk
Web site: www.youngminds.org.uk
Young Minds, the national association for children's mental health. Produces a range of leaflets, reports, magazine and newsletters. Parents Information Line: 0800 0182138.

INDEX

★★★★★

The Internet has been likened to shopping in a supermarket without aisles. The press of a button on a Web browser can bring up thousands of sites but working your way through them to find what you want can involve long and frustrating on-line searches.

And unfortunately many sites contain inaccurate, misleading or heavily biased information. Our researchers have therefore undertaken an extensive analysis to bring you a selection of quality Web site addresses.

Befrienders International
www.befrienders.org
Befrienders International, with a head office in London, is a network of 357 befriending centres world-wide. Click on the Information button for articles on the following: when someone is suicidal, helping a friend, myths about suicide, about depression and warning signs.

Mental Health Foundation
www.mentalhealth.org.uk
A useful web site which has information on self-harm including the following: definitions, statistics and dispelling myths. Also has contact information for relevant organisations including the National Self-harm Network.

National Depression Campaign
www.depressionalliance.org
Entering the word 'suicide' in the Search box on this site will produce a range of useful articles and factsheets on depression.

ChildLine
www.childline.org.uk
ChildLine is the UK's free national helpline for children and young people in trouble or danger. They provides useful advice for young people who have lost a relative of friend. Click on Children and Young People button and scroll to the bottom of the page. Click on Search and enter the word 'suicide' in the search box. This brings up a number of relevant ChildLine factsheets on suicide. If you want to talk to someone, call ChildLine free on 0800 1111.

The Samaritans
www.samaritans.org.uk
The Samaritans is based in the UK and the Republic of Ireland. It provides confidential emotional support to any person who is suicidal or despairing. Click on The Samaritans Youth Pack link for a range of invaluable information. Click on Suicide in the UK and Ireland on their main menu for information about: suicide statistics, suicide and occupation, young people and suicide, older people and suicide, attempted suicide and prison suicides.

ACKNOWLEDGEMENTS

The publisher is grateful for permission to reproduce the following material.

While every care has been taken to trace and acknowledge copyright, the publisher tenders its apology for any accidental infringement or where copyright has proved untraceable. The publisher would be pleased to come to a suitable arrangement in any such case with the rightful owner.

Chapter One: Suicide and Self-harm

Suicide and attempted suicide, © 2000 Royal College of Psychiatrists, *Half of all women 'think of suicide'*, © Telegraph Group Limited, London 2000, *Defining suicide*, © The Samaritans, 2000, *Suicidal behaviour in children and young people*, © Kidscape, *Key facts: attempted suicide*, © The Samaritans, 1999, *Attempted suicide/deliberate self-harm*, © Crown copyright is reproduced with the permission of the Controller of Her Majesty's Stationery Office, *Deliberate self-harm in young people*, © 2000 Royal College of Psychiatrists, *How many people self-harm?*, © Mental Health Foundation, 2000, *Worried about self-injury?*, © Young Minds, *Self-harm*, © Mental Health Foundation, *Analysing suicide statistics*, © Source unattributable, *Suicide and race*, © MIND, *Suicide and mental health*, © Mental Health Foundation, 1999, *Causes of suicide*, © Mental Health Foundation, 2000, *Key facts on suicide*, © MIND, *Suicide in older people*, © MIND, *Suicide in prisons*, © MIND, *Self-inflicted deaths in prison*, © The Samaritans, © *Jail suicide rate doubles in 15 years*, © The Independent, May 1999, *Steep rise in suicides worries jail reformers*, © The Guardian, July 1999, *Copycat suicides and media reporting*, © The Samaritans.

Chapter Two: Seeking Help

Helping distressed young people, © Trust for the Study of Adolescence, *Suicide in young people*, © ONS, GRO (Scotland), GRO (N. Ireland), Crown copyright is reproduced with the permission of the Controller of Her Majesty's Stationery Office, *How do I know if someone close to me is suicidal?*, © MIND, *Not just a 'cry for help'*, © PAPYRUS, *Befrienders International*, © 2000 Befrienders International, *Working together for the prevention of young suicide*, © PAPYRUS, *Helping young people*, © The Samaritans, *Suicide rates*, © World Health Organisation, 2000, *Suicide and young people*, © ChildLine, *Poster alert over suicide epidemic in young men*, © Telegraph Group Limited, London 1999, *Signs of suicide risk*, © The Samaritans, *Men behaving sadly*, © 2000 Royal College of Psychiatrists, *Samaritans launch online schools pack*, © Courtesy of BBC News Online, *Doctors declare war on male suicides*, © Courtesy of BBC News Online, *Drive to reduce suicides*, © Courtesy of BBC News Online, *Saving lives: mental health*, © Crown copyright is reproduced with the permission of the Controller of Her Majesty's Stationery Office, *Death rates from suicide*, © World Health Organisation (WHO), *Prevention of suicidal behaviours*, © World Health Organisation (WHO), *Losing someone we love*, © CRUSE, *Supporting a child who is bereaved through suicide*, © Winston's Wish.

Photographs and illustrations:

Pages 1, 3, 12, 22, 26, 31, 39: Pumpkin House, pages 16, 25, 33, 37, 38, 40: Simon Kneebone.

Craig Donnellan
Cambridge
May, 2000